ONE IN TEN HAD TO DIE

It was strangely calm: no wind, and the sea as smooth as a mirror. *Anna*'s Second Mate examined the water, using his binoculars. That was how he noticed the glistening track furrowing the surface, heading straight for the *Anna*. He gave a terrible cry, and pointed at the torpedo track.

The Skipper acted instantly, putting the engine room telegraph to full speed ahead. But it was not possible to turn *Anna* through ninety degrees before the torpedo drew level. The Skipper gripped the rail and watched – watched the line of bubbles disappearing beneath *Anna*'s stern . . .

Also in Fontana

Skis Against the Atom *Knut Haukelid*
Two Eggs on My Plate *Olut Reed Olsen*
Report from No. 24 *Gunnar Sonsteby*

PER HANSSON

One in Ten Had to Die

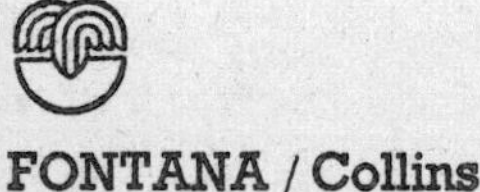

FONTANA / Collins

First published in 1970 by George Allen & Unwin Ltd
First issued in Fontana Books 1975

Translated from *Hver Tiende Mann Matte Dφ*

Printed in Canada

PART ONE

Six and thirty grey ships on a grey sea beneath a grey sky.

Aboard these thirty-six ships more than a thousand men in constant expectation of being torpedoed.

Old ships and new ships, small ships and large, heading for England at seven knots. In was now six days and nights since they had left the coast of America.

Morning came on the seventh day and the low cloud became thinner and thinner. Now and again the look-out on the wing of the bridge could see the sun looking like a pale moon in the south-east.

The surface of the sea was the colour of lead and without a ripple; the Atlantic was strangely calm and if anyone spoke it was in low tones. The slightest unexpected sound made people start, and when in one of the steamers a seaman dropped a bucket and it rolled clattering over the deck, his shipmates cursed furiously.

Six ships in each column, with the sea so calm that the foam and bubbles from their bow-waves and propellers floated in their wake for a long time – their wakes trailed like veils behind them, mourning veils.

It was a slow convoy and radio silence had been imposed. Everything had to be done with the least possible noise because packs of enemy U-boats were lying in wait equipped with listening-apparatus. Many men in many of the ships could count on being dead by the time the next watch began: every mile on was a step nearer the grave.

The air was mild and there was no wind, yet never since the first tiny craft crossed that great ocean centuries ago, had it been more dangerous to be in the Atlantic.

*

On this seventh day after the convoy had sailed from New York a group of middle-aged and older men, some in civilian clothes, some in uniform, were making calculations in a room with dark walls in London's Parliament Street. When they had finished and checked their work, sitting round a large oak table, it showed that in the previous months on average one Allied merchant ship had been sunk every four hours.

The men were never told these calculations. They just saw ships going down until the day they went down themselves and became just figures in the calculations of the grave-faced men seated around that oak table in their room in London. If they chanced to survive another 'crossing' they would prefer to be kept in ignorance of all these calculations when they got ashore.

Most of them gathered around the bars in the dock area, not wanting to go any farther, because in the streets and parks and restaurants that lay beyond, places that were not there just for seamen, they felt insecure, unwelcome.

It was on the seventh day out that a Norwegian boat developed engine trouble and dropped behind. Nobody was allowed to stop. The convoy had to stick to its course and speed even when men from a sunken ship were struggling in the water, shouting for help. Only the rescue-boat, the last in the convoy, and the escort vessels were allowed to stop to pick up survivors. A stationary ship was an easy target for the enemy, especially if their attackers were many and daring: it was more likely that the ship would be sunk than the men rescued. And when the escort vessel was not moving the surviving ships in the convoy were without its protection.

That was why in many convoys men from torpedoed ships were left to drown, left to stare at the ships as they steamed away, until the last stern had disappeared below the horizon.

If this happened in the north Atlantic or Arctic, the men aboard the lucky ships hoped that those in the water would hasten their end by stripping off their life-jackets, otherwise they would freeze to death and then drift around in the icy currents providing food for birds and fish.

On the seventh day after the convoy left New York the weather was quite summery. An hour after the Norwegian boat had lagged helplessly behind, the U-boat alarm sounded. Electric bells and wailing sirens tore at the men's ear-drums. Those who were off watch hurried from cabins to their stations. The sound waves from an escort vessel's asdic had picked up a grey U-boat hull in the depths, and the echo returning to the sensitive machine sent its ping-ping signal as a warning that the enemy was close at hand.

The two corvettes began the hunt, circling like sheepdogs around their flock, dropping depth-charges to scare off the enemy submarines.

Explosions boomed from the deep. The men in the engine-rooms of the merchant ships felt them like gigantic hammer-blows on the ship's bottom and those on deck saw columns of water being thrown into the air.

Anna was in the centre of the convoy.

She was an old ship, laden with shells, bombs, tinned foods, dynamite, nitro-glycerine and cases of ammunition, weighing thousands of tons. To avoid accidents the American dockers had worn thick woollen socks over their boots when they loaded her. Her crew now went about in life-jackets but only because that was the rule. If *Anna* was hit by a torpedo, within seconds she would be transformed into an exploding sea of flame that none could expect to survive.

'We'll be blown into tiny pieces,' AB said to Bo'sun, throwing his life-jacket on to the deck.

'Put it on again. It'll keep you warm as you speed up to heaven,' said the Bo'sun.

AB kicked at the life-jacket irritably and said, 'The naval officer at that course in New York had one single drop of nitro-glycerine in a glass tube. A tiny drop it was. You could scarcely see it, but it made the hell of a bang. In the containers below deck there must be hundreds of gallons of it. Yes, hundreds of gallons of nitro-glycerine in the hold right under our feet . . .'

'Oh shut your trap,' said Bo'sun, but there was no anger in his voice. 'If we start on that we'll all go crazy before we're half-way across.'

'But think of all that nitro. And the tons of explosives and ammunition . . .' the AB repeated.

But the Bo'sun did not reply, he just bent down and picked up the life-jacket. And because it was so surprising that Bo'sun should pick it up, AB decided he had better keep his mouth shut as long as he could.

Shortly afterwards there was an explosion somewhere ahead and then they saw that the Commodore of Convoy's ship had been hit.

It was as if an invisible giant fist had thrust down on the ship and broken it in two. Bow and stern rose up out of the water like a huge frayed V.

Someone in *Anna* shouted, 'Torpedo approaching!' The Bo'sun and the AB spun round, but could not see any bubbles.

Again they turned to look for'ard and see what was happening to the Commodore's ship but it was already below the surface on its way to the depths of the ocean.

Another loud bang. This time it was a Danish boat that had been hit. They knew she was Danish, were in a way chummy with her, because *Anna* had been following in her wake ever since they left New York. Slowly the Dane heeled over, and a row of men went slowly down and down in the lifeboat.

The torpedo had hit the forepart and now the bows began to sink while the stern rose clear of the water. The propeller was racing wildly as it came out of the water. The lifeboat that had been lowered had not got clear of the ship's side, and in *Anna* they could hear the men shouting as their boat was drawn towards the glinting propeller. The blades, over a yard long, guillotined the man on the for'ard thwart. The others had flung themselves down into the bottom of the boat.

The bows of the torpedoed ship sank lower. The propeller was now whirling inches above the lifeboat. Suddenly the bow-wave from one of the other ships swept across and lifted the lifeboat, and the swishing blades chopped it to smithereens.

It was strangely calm: no wind and a swell so slight that the sea was as smooth as a mirror, thought *Anna*'s Second Mate. He examined the water, using his binoculars to pick up every detail. That was how he noticed the glistening track furrowing the surface, heading straight for *Anna*. He bellowed, nothing comprehensible, just a yell, for fright had paralysed his powers of speech. With trembling hand he pointed at the torpedo track.

The Skipper acted instantly, putting the engine-room telegraph to emergency full speed ahead; and it was as if fear had given the men below second sight, as if their eyes could pierce the ship's thin side and see the approaching torpedo. In a matter of seconds the engines were going all out and the whole ship was shaking under the strain. And before the Skipper had time even to give the order, the helmsman had spun the wheel hard to port.

It was not possible to turn *Anna* through ninety degrees before the torpedo drew level; if it had been, it would perhaps have passed down the ship's side; but with the extra speed and the wheel hard over there was just a chance of it passing astern.

The Skipper took a firm grip on the rail, pressed his foot against the deck – and watched. As he watched the bubbles disappear under the stern his hair stood on end. But he did not shut his eyes: he continued to stare fixedly astern until he saw the track of the torpedo furrowing the surface on the other side. It was so close that it looked as if it had just been fired from *Anna*. It sped on towards the ships in the next column.

The Skipper was trembling all over. He continued to clutch on to the rail, so that the helmsman and look-out should not see.

In manœuvring to avoid the torpedo *Anna* had found herself among the ships in the convoy's port wing.

Shouts of 'Collision!' came from the look-out as a huge grey ship closed *Anna*'s stern. *Anna*'s gun crew made a dash from the poop towards the boat-deck. There was a crash, and *Anna* quivered and creaked, the bows of the big ship hanging over her stern. Then, with the splintering of hull and deck cargo and the scraping of steel, the two ships let go of each other.

The Skipper ran down from the bridge and made for the stern to inspect the damage. When he reached the poop, the Bo'sun was already there, but before either spoke, the Skipper realized that *Anna* had got off lightly.

'A miracle!' the Skipper said.

'More than that,' Bo'sun replied. 'Furst the torpedo, and now no explosion in the cargo following the collision . . .'

The ship that had run into *Anna* had clipper bows, and the Skipper was delighted to see that apart from a few plates stove in high up, a short length of rail damaged, and the flagpole missing, *Anna* was completely seaworthy.

The Skipper felt a sudden deep affection for his ship and for the Chief Officer and crew, but he showed no signs of his feelings. Curtly he gave the Bo'sun an order to fix up the plates and rail as well as could be done at sea. As he returned to the bridge he appeared very calm.

'Starboard a little,' and *Anna* resumed her place in the line. With quivering hands the crew lit up their cigarettes, inhaling deeply and greedily.

They had resumed their place in the line when there was another bang to starboard, this time ahead.

A small Norwegian steamer had been hit in the engine-room, her boilers had exploded, tearing the hull up amidships.

Could they hear the screams of the men being scalded and boiled below deck? Was it one long drawn-out cry of torment or was it the grey steam hissing and shrieking as it escaped from the torn pipes?

The ill-fated ship rolled over before any lifeboats or rafts could reach the water, showing half her bottom to *Anna*'s column and striking her masts against the water. Four figures scrambled out on to her side which was now just about horizontal. They stood up and yelled, waving their arms.

The Bo'sun and the AB reacted simultaneously. They ran up the ladder to the bridge and almost shouted into the Skipper's face: 'We must save them!'

'We are not allowed to stop,' was the reply.

The AB caught hold of the Skipper's jacket. 'Stop!' he begged. 'We must stop!'

The Skipper thrust the hand away. 'I have my orders,' he said, but he was not looking at either man, but staring hard in front of him at the other ships farther up the column.

'You shit!' AB shouted as he left the bridge.

The Bo'sun said nothing. He took a couple of steps towards the boat-deck, then paused and looked pleadingly at the Skipper. But the Skipper had his back turned and was staring ahead. He did not look at the sinking steamer again. She rolled right over to lie with her masts pointing to the bottom, while the four men crawled up her slippery red bottom towards the keel, clawing at the green-covered plates.

It was as if the old boat was determined not to leave the surface and the light of day. The four men were still lying across her keel when *Anna*'s look out shouted: 'Torpedo astern!'

The Skipper had been standing as if rooted to the deck

staring for'ard ever since Bo'sun and AB had left him, but now as he turned swiftly he noticed a torpedo ripping the surface. He could see that it would pass close astern of *Anna* and that it was heading straight towards the capsized ship.

The four men on the steamer's bottom had also seen the streak on the surface. Mouths agape, they scrambled along the keel to the stern, clawing with their nails at shells and weed. It was as if they were running on their knees, while the torpedo hissed towards the wreck.

Bo'sun turned his eyes away just before the explosion. He forced himself to think of drink and his Liverpool bar. He had been at sea a long time and had his favourite bars in every port. It gave him a feeling of homecoming when the publican and barmaids welcomed him back and he spent lavishly out of sheer gratitude at being recognized.

If he survived this trip, he was thinking, he would drink as much as he could swallow, spend his every penny on whisky and beer, drown in alcohol all thoughts of the victims of burning ships, exploding ships, capsizing ships, doomed men and dead men . . . Since he began sailing in convoys he had not needed anything ashore but spirits and beer. He could not be bothered to save or buy things of lasting value. Like so many others he went ashore in trousers and shirt during the summer and when the wintry air was raw and foggy he would be content with just a jacket or a jersey. Like so many others he considered it merely stupid to possess more than one suit and a few shirts and perhaps a light overcoat. They were always expecting to be torpedoed, always having to count on their ship going down. And you could not take suits or overcoats or hats with you from a tanker that was enveloped in flames or from an exploding ammunition ship. You would not have the chance to buy yourself any more suits or ties if your ship was laden with petrol or nitro-glycerine or bombs, as was this one. And if you made a trip without explosive cargo, you knew you were one of the elect if you were not maimed or killed by the torpedo or bomb that struck your ship . . . one of the elect if you saved your skin and got on a raft. There were men who shared each other's shaving brush and razor, because they did not wish to throw their money away on anything that could not provide them with forgetfulness or amusement during the short time they spent ashore.

Many went on the binge for as long as they could. If they still had money left when the time came to sail again, they gave handfuls of it to the girls or to someone they had noticed sitting for hours over one glass of beer, whose face would light up at such a gift from a strange sailor who scarcely spoke English.

A few did try to save part of their modest wages. They either had faith in surviving convoy work, or they saved because a slowly growing sum was necessary for their day-dreams. *Anna*'s wireless operator was one of these. He helped the months to pass by planning the big radio business he was going to start at home as soon as the war was over. 'Sparks' was accumulating what he called his 'starting capital' and when the ship was in port he bought quantities of books on electronics which he read at sea when he had fear under control. He was always planning what he was going to have in his shop, which grew bigger and bigger with every crossing of the Atlantic.

In *Anna* no one looked askance at a person who saved. That was regarded as his own affair, as long as he did not try to avoid standing his round in the bars when he was ashore with the others. But one or two were worried by those who let their pay accumulate – having got it into their heads that the saver was challenging something dangerous and nameless. They would not admit to being superstitious and never spoke of it in the mess, but they had heard that people who saved got killed more quickly than those who spent their every penny in bars.

Bo'sun's thoughts went back to the spirits and beer he was going to pour down his throat if he survived this trip. He would go to the bar, his bar, and stay there until his pockets were empty – if he survived . . .

Before signing on in *Anna* Bo'sun had had a safe shore job, with firm ground under his feet, for several months. But all the time he had felt a shirker: in the yard, in the streets, in restaurants and in houses among people who did not know what convoys were. He had walked about thinking of those at sea – had stretched out in the good bed in his rented room and been uncomfortable because he could not help thinking of those others who lay sleepless in their bunks and fo'c'sles. He had sat on benches in the park, yet he had found no joy in the trees and grass and flowers because his head had been full of thoughts of those who sat on the boat-deck all night not daring to go between-decks.

Anna's crew had heard Bo'sun's stories about those three months he had spent ashore after being torpedoed. He had suffered minor injuries and some kind-hearted person in authority had decided that he should have a shore job until further notice. Qualified people were hard to find in wartime England and he got a good job in a shipyard. Time and again the Bo'sun told them of the good wages the yard had paid him, and his comfortable little room, and how he would never have set foot on another deck if the damned authorities had not decided that he must go to sea again. He made a great thing of 'the glorious time' he had had ashore and of his rage with the authorities. The men liked this tack, especially when he cursed the people who sat in offices; it gave them a sense of solidarity. They shared his fury, and never stopped thinking up accusations to bring up against the 'desk wallahs'.

Bo'sun was lying, of course, but he convinced the men in *Anna*. For one reason or another he would have been allowed to stay ashore, but he could not stand it because he was not at peace with himself. Sometimes in the yard during the day or down in the harbour in the evening he thought he heard someone calling to him from the sea. One Sunday when the fog lay close inshore, the calling had been so insistent that he had gone right to the edge of the quay to get as near as possible to whoever it was out there.

While he was working ashore, two of the ships he had sailed in had gone down, and he heard of others being sunk, ships carrying men whom he knew, with whom he had sailed, worked, squabbled and laughed, stood drinks to and had been stood drinks by.

He had felt such a mean pig ashore.

He had joined *Anna* because she had happened to be in port when he decided he could no longer bear feeling a shirker. He often felt bitter at having to sail in these convoys, and he never saw himself as a person who was willing to give his life for someone or something. It was just that he could not stay ashore when the others had to go to sea.

Wouldn't he just get drunk, if *Anna* managed to get across again!

He liked British ports best. In the States and other countries he felt that the people were just after his money, but in England it was different, even in the pubs. You came from New York where the streets and buildings were all lit up, where things were booming and everything the heart could desire was to be had in profusion, and arrived in Liverpool or Newcastle, or perhaps Cardiff or even London, and there it was all black-out, bombing, fires and rationing.

In British ports the men from the convoys were greeted with gratitude and understanding. They did not pay more than the landlubbers for whisky, strictly rationed as it was, but often were allowed to have it all, while the locals standing beside them made do with beer and considered it right that they should. Often the pub girls would get up from the tables where they had been sitting with American sailors who had pockets stuffed with dollars, and go to sit with the Norwegians who earned only a quarter as much. The last time they were in Liverpool the men from *Anna* had been greeted by 'Convoy Molly' in Bo'sun's favourite bar with 'Here are the Norwegians – the real sailors!' and they had felt far more honoured by her welcome than by all the fine words bestowed on them by the politicians.

When the girls left the Americans, who could pay four times more than the Norwegians for a drink and an hour in a dingy hotel room or bedsitter, it gave the men from the *Anna* and other Norwegian ships a feeling of being preferred – of being less exploited than the others.

Bo'sun started as a pattern of depth-charges exploded near *Anna*. He stared at the line of ships to starboard and port, and the craving for alcohol was like an ache in his belly.

But it was only seven days since they had left New York and this was a slow convoy. And there was no longer any doubt that a whole pack of U-boats was after them. They might attack at any moment – or wait until dusk, night, or the grey dawn.

Bo'sun was accustomed to being afraid; fear was as much a part of convoy work as wearing a life-jacket. But that day as he sat on No. 3 hatch he fell prey to something even worse than fear – the numbing weight of hopelessness. He ought to go and take a better look at the damage to the stern – he had had orders from the Skipper to do so – but he had stayed where he was on the hatch while *Anna* ploughed on through mile after mile of calm water.

Many on board felt the same choking fear and hopelessness. They had scarcely moved since the little Norwegian steamer had rolled over, and they had stood watching their fellow countrymen crawling desperately along the steamer's slippery red bottom without being able to lift a finger to help them. They did not talk together; they could think of nothing but torpedoes, explosions, spurting flames and death, and those at home, and drink by the gallon and whether there was a God in heaven . . .

The Carpenter got up and made his way over to the chart-house, and from there to the boat-deck. Then he was seen going aft with an oar in one hand and a flag in the other. From many parts of *Anna* eyes were fixed on this big dungaree-clad figure striding across the deck. He stopped by the stern rail, nailed and lashed the oar to it, and the next minute a new Norwegian flag was fluttering bravely in the breeze.

The Skipper had watched it all from the bridge, and now his hand relaxed their convulsive grip of the rail; he found himself thinking that they ought to have had a new flag long before this. The old one which the clipper bow had shorn off in the collision had been lashed and frayed by rain and wind and weather. The new flag with its fresh colours made everything seem better. All eyes were now fixed on that flag.

Not long afterwards two more ships were torpedoed on the starboard wing of the convoy, but *Anna* kept her course.

There was now no longer a convoy with nice straight columns. No signals were being sent from the other ships, and the Skipper concluded that the Vice-Commodore's ship had been sunk as well, sharing the fate of the convoy-leader, a retired British admiral now at the bottom of the sea.

The two escort vessels were racing round the convoy with black flags to signify that depth-charges were about to be dropped. They were corvettes, being handled with unbelievable skill and daring; tearing around in bigger or small circles, dashing off at a tangent and making turns so sharp that the spray from their bow-waves was washing down their fo'c'sles. But it was almost hopeless to try to find and deal with so many torpedoes. When the corvettes were busy on one side of the convoy a ship would be hit on the other, or astern or right for'ard. Then their powerful engines would send them racing in the direction of the latest attack; but before they got there, other U-boats could have struck at the ship they had just left.

The corvettes' 'ear' was the asdic with its 'ping-ping' signals. If the asdic picked up an echo depth-charges had to be dropped, even if men from a torpedoed ship were floating in their life-jackets nearby . . . The Navy had to conform to the cruel dictates of war, whose first commandment was: sink or be sunk!

The U-boats had to be driven away or destroyed before they had time to torpedo more ships each with thousands of tons of war materials and food for the Allied forces and hard-pressed Britain, and before still more sailors were blown to pieces, roasted in a sea of flame, scalded in an engine-room or forced to abandon ship.

The Navy had no choice. If it did not use its depth-charges because it did not want to risk bursting the lungs and stomachs of Allied seamen floating in their life-jackets, it was just giving the Germans a free hand to sink what they liked in the convoy. But for every depth-charge the men had to drop, something in their own minds went, something that would never be mended. A man who had seen people lying on the surface with split bellies like dynamited fish, and who helped to drop the depth-charge that caused it, was never the same again.

Anna's Skipper looked at his watch. It was half an hour now since the last ship had been struck. He nodded to the helmsman and attempted a smile of encouragement. But he knew that the U-boats would attack again and again. They never let go of a convoy while they had torpedoes and fuel left, and only a couple of hours had passed since the first ship was sunk.

The convoy had more than another ten days in the Atlantic before the English coast would emerge, and on the last stretch they could also expect to be attacked by bombers from bases on the Continent. Swarms of planes would come diving out of the sky, raining bombs on the ships, and when they had dropped all their bombs they would swoop over them again and again, raking the decks with their machine-guns.

Anna had a couple of light machine-guns and an old gun aft, but that did not give her any real chance of fighting a dive-bomber or a machine-gunning plane roaring past at mast-head height. There had been talk for a long time of getting an ack-ack gun, and before they left New York they had sent an urgent request to Nortraship for a Bofors gun for *Anna*. They had all signed it – first the Skipper, then the other officers, and then the crew, and right at the bottom was the ship's boy's name written in his childish handwriting . . .

It was an hour now since the last attack. The First Mate thought that eight ships had been sunk. The Skipper swept the water with his glasses, but the columns were still too scattered for him to count the ships. By late afternoon the convoy had resumed formation and when the Skipper counted again, ten ships were missing. And this was just the end of the seventh day! Ten ships gone out of thirty-six!

They expected a new attack at any moment and no one in *Anna* lay down in his bunk, nor could anyone bring himself to sit in the mess to eat. No one dared go below, each man just took a sandwich or something up on deck and ate it there – if he could get it down. They spoke little if at all, but now and again someone would try to start a conversation about women or the last binge in New York – or other binges in Liverpool or Cardiff, or about the strangely calm weather they were having on this trip. But the words did not penetrate the consciousness of the others. They heard the voice, heard the words, but fear filled their minds, paralysing their brains so that they were not able to grasp what was being said.

Even the one who was talking had no real contact with his own words. They just issued from his mouth, a dry mouth that required a few gulps of coffee before it sounded more or less normal.

They all had this feeling of fear. Those not on the watch stayed on the boat-deck. And those whose watch it was on deck or in the engine-room remained in the same places and in the same attitudes for long periods at a time, staring automatically at piston, lever, pipe or gauge, or at the silhouettes of other ships or the smooth surface of the sea, which could at anv moment and in any place be disturbed by the tracks of torpedoes.

They all waited, every man alone with his fear.

Evening came and night fell; some of them lay on the floor in the mess while others preferred that of the galley amidships, from both of which they could reach the boat-deck in a matter of seconds and where there was warmth from the engines underneath and a coffee-pot within reach. Some who were off watch sat on the boat-deck with their backs against the funnels or beside a lifeboat, thinking of torpedoes.

All night the men in these twenty-six ships waited, while the two corvettes hunted tirelessly through the darkness searching for U-boats. Towards morning of the eighth day, when the light returned, they drew deeper breaths and many of them discovered that they were aching all over.

At eight-thirty on the morning of that eighth day there was another explosion.

The weather was the same, sunny and fine with an almost smooth sea and a blue autumn sky. How many men that day were to see a trail of bubbles on the glassy surface and then be maimed or killed?

The U-boats attacked from two directions simultaneously. Ships exploded, ships broke in two, ships rolled over on their sides. Men were torn to ribbons, burned like torches on the deck of a tanker. Some got into lifeboats and on to rafts, while others floundered in the calm, grey water. Some came within reach of the propellers of other boats ahead, others were flung half out of the water by the force of depth-charges exploding beneath them. If they were not already unconscious or dead, they sank at once with mouths gaping because all the air had been squeezed out of their lungs. They swallowed salt water and oil from torpedoed ships and the thick oil stuck in throat and lungs, choked them and blinded them.

The muzzles of merchant ships' guns were raised and lowered, swung this way and that as the men thought they saw a periscope breaking the surface here or there, but few shots were fired. The enemy was invisible.

Then an ammunition ship was hit.

Suddenly there was an enormous orange flame and the air quivered as thousands of tons of bombs, shells, nitro-glycerine and other explosives went sky high. A column of white smoke hung round the fire and when the light breeze had swept the smoke away there was nothing to be seen except froth and steam. The ship must have carried a similar cargo to *Anna*.

The *Anna*'s Carpenter, who had attended a brief gunnery course at home, was head of the crew of six that manned an aged weapon on the poop. The Carpenter had been very industrious on that course, scarcely allowing himself time for a beer. Now he fussed over *Anna*'s gun every day, guarding it like a jealous dog, and, except when they were practising, not allowing anyone to lay so much as a finger on his precious twenty-five-pounder. Whenever the opportunity offered, he would throw an empty cask into the sea and use it as a target.

Now the Carpenter was sitting in the gunlayer's seat, eyes pressed close to the telescopic sight. He was watching one of the corvettes firing a pattern of depth-charges. Immediately after the explosion patches of oil appeared on the surface. A hit!

Yelling with delight, *Anna*'s crew stood watching the damaged U-boat surface, but as the ugly grey hull slowly emerged their fear grew. All at once they fell silent.

Before the U-boat's deck was properly clear of the water,

Germans had emerged from the conning-tower and, clinging to the rail as they waded up to their knees in water, were making for the gun on the forepart. The next moment the U-boat was firing at the corvette which separated it from *Anna*.

The Carpenter spat furiously. He dared not shoot because the shell could just as easily have hit the corvette as the U-boat. All at once the corvette seemed to receive a mighty slap which made her heel right over. When she righted herself there was a gaping hole in her bows just above the water-line. As she was no longer heading straight for the U-boat, which was still firing its automatic cannon, *Anna*'s gun had a clear line of fire. The Carpenter and his men got to work quickly and deftly, but they had to get the gun trained properly. The Carpenter held his fire, waiting until he had calculated *Anna*'s speed, the angle and all the other things he had been taught on the gunnery course. Now! He fired, a cloud of smoke appeared on the U-boat's deck. At the sight of it the Norwegians all yelled, a loud, savage yell.

Feverishly they got ready for another shot, but before they had time to fire again the wind had blown the smoke clear and they saw that the U-boat's gun and its crew had been swept away. They fired one more shell, but it fell wide of the U-boat, and by the time they were ready to fire again the corvette had finished her off.

The attack stopped abruptly after half an hour, and by midday the convoy had reformed and resumed its old course. This time it was easier for the *Anna*'s Skipper to count the ships. There were seventeen. So far, nineteen had been hit and sunk in eight days. Thirty-six had sailed from New York, and it was more than ten days before they would sight the coast of Britain.

The Skipper had been on his feet ever since the first boat in the convoy was sunk, hurrying to and fro about the wheel-house and bridge for more than twenty-four hours. Now he came down the ladder into his cabin.

He surveyed his grimy, bearded face in the mirror. His hands were trembling as he began to shave. As he scraped the lather off with his razor, it struck him that perhaps he need not bother. Half the convoy already lay at the bottom of the Atlantic and every nerve in his body told him that the attacks were going to continue.

It would still be many days and nights before they reached port, if any of them did. He gazed at the mirror and thought that perhaps he might not even live long enough to wipe his face clean. But it was refreshing to have the stiff stubble removed and it would help morale aboard if the Skipper was as well turned out as he could be.

The mirror showed that the furrows at the corners of his mouth had deepened. A nerve was quivering visibly beneath the skin on his left cheek. He pressed his hand to the place to stop the quivering and when that did not work, he dipped a towel into hot and cold water alternately and laid it on his cheek. He did not dare stretch out on his sofa. He was too full of fear and weighed down by responsibility to be able to relax.

He opened the cupboard and produced a bottle of whisky, rang for the steward, and told him to take a glass each to the men serving the gun on the poop. From another bottle he poured himself two stiff pegs in the hope of stopping the trembling of his hands before he went to clink glasses with the gun's crew. Then he looked to see that his jacket was properly buttoned, then went out and walked quietly to the poop to drink with the crew and praise them for hitting the U-boat.

This was the first time apart from Christmas and the country's National Day that he had given the men a drink at sea. He had decided that they should all have a glass, but the gun's crew should have theirs first, and so feel that they had been singled out for special honour and reward. He would then wait a while before the others got theirs, letting them have plenty of time to ponder on the unusual behaviour of the Skipper giving anyone a drink at sea. After a while those who had not worked the gun would become irritated and feel hurt at not having been given one too. He knew what they would be thinking: 'We've done our job too!' The men below decks would mutter peevishly that a gun would have been no help if they hadn't kept the engines up to the mark, and the helmsman and cook and steward and all the others would think the same of their jobs. This feeling of being unjustly treated would perhaps make them forget their fear and despair for a while, so he wanted to keep them irritated as long as he could, so that their minds would be off torpedoes and painful death. When, in half an hour or so, he went to the men in the galley and on deck and to all those who had not worked the gun, and thanked them for the way they did their jobs, he knew they would feel encouraged and be grateful.

It was only the Second Mate who went without his tot on that eighth day out. While the Skipper was on the poop drinking with the gun's crew, the Second Mate had climbed into the port lifeboat. He sat down on the thwart where he stayed motionless staring straight ahead. His gaze was as rigid as that of a dead man and his hands lay lifeless on top of a small suitcase on his knees. The Skipper spoke to him, poured him out a glass, but he did not reply and not a muscle in his hands moved when the glass was held up to him.

It was the middle of the day and the sun quite hot, but the Second Mate was wearing his sheepskin coat under his life-jacket and still looked as though he felt cold. He did not respond to the Skipper's friendly voice, but when the glass was thrust almost into his hand he slowly withdrew his arm. Otherwise he seemed paralysed with fear.

The Skipper left the whisky bottle beside the lifeboat and told the steward to have food and coffee brought to the mate.

From all over the ship men were gazing at the lifeboat in which one of their officers sat motionless, hour after hour. They were already haunted by the fear of fresh U-boat attacks and now the Second Mate's breakdown made them think that the same thing might happen to them. They had not noticed anything peculiar about the Second Mate until this had happened. He had never had much to say, so the fact that during the last couple of days he had scarcely opened his mouth had not attracted attention.

The men for'ard and aft tried not to look at the port lifeboat and the figure motionless on the thwart like a huge doll, but their eyes kept going back to it. They felt they wanted to force him down to the bottom boards so that at least they could not see him, a man frozen in fear. They could have knocked him unconscious and shut him up in the sick-bay, done anything to get this motionless, dumb figure out of their sight, but the Skipper had said that he was to be left alone, reckoning that a man whom fear had driven to get into the lifeboat while it hung in its davits was not likely to jump over the side.

The ship's Carpenter had been feeling very important since the *Anna* had shot that U-boat, and he had hoped that the Skipper would have given him an extra tot of whisky. But one whisky was certainly better than none, he thought, as he stood in the stern patting the grey gun barrel. He was still feeling pleased as it was the first time they had been able to fire at an enemy and, though he had known what he was doing, it was little short of a miracle that the shell had struck the U-boat's deck.

They had had the gun a long time now and it had become as much a matter of course and part of the ship as the derricks and hatches, bitts and chains. But the Carpenter remembered the naïve ideas they had had about the gun at first and he would always remember the day it came aboard.

An icy wind was blowing into Liverpool harbour, where they were in dock for repairs after a stormy crossing of the Atlantic. *Anna*'s wheel had been damaged when they were still several days away from the coast of England and the convoy had just abandoned *Anna*, so that she had dropped farther and farther astern until she was alone and defenceless. She had crawled along in waters where the Germans were sinking Allied ships every day. The men had waited for disaster to strike, but not spoken much about the dangers in the air above and in the water beneath.

They had had as little liking for talk of U-boats and torpedoes then as they did now, feeling that the very words could call down the devil upon them, that it was enough to say torpedo or U-boat aloud to draw the enemy's attention to old *Anna*. But that time when they fell behind the convoy, they had talked often and vehemently about the craziness of going on sailing the Atlantic without anything with which to defend themselves. They had raged at the authorities who gave them orders to bring their forces bombs, aeroplanes, tanks, shells and other war material in their holds and on their decks, while the crew were not given as much as a machine-gun to defend ship and cargo against German planes and U-boats. They had talked of getting a heavy Bofors gun to protect them from aerial attack, but most of all they wanted a gun that could scare a U-boat away or at least give *Anna* a chance in a fight. In those days many of them had considerable hopes of surviving; indeed, most had felt sure that they would get home if only they were given the means to defend themselves in a scrape. The war was still new to the men in *Anna* then. She had crawled along and managed to reach Liverpool, and the Skipper had gone to the shipping office and banged his fist on the table and demanded a gun for *Anna*. And they had listened to the Skipper! Some Navy men had come aboard and the boat had seethed with excitement. They were going to have a gun! No one had bothered about the icy wind from the Irish Sea, they had all hurried up from mess and bunk and stood in their thin clothes on the poop watching. The steward and cook had abandoned the galley and even the engine-room staff had appeared on deck to share in the great event.

The mounting was ready and the gun shipped. It was steel grey and at least ten feet long. They had all felt strong and important. They no longer served in a defenceless hulk. The *Anna* had become dangerous, a little bit of a warship – so they had thought in those days, when the war was still young. First they had stood aft offering each other cigarettes and then they had all gone up and touched it, sliding a hand caressingly over the steel muzzle. The instructor had come aboard to show them how to use it, while the Skipper watched, cap pulled well down over his forehead so that the glossy black peak had made his tired blue eyes look even more tired. Oil-spattered men from the engine-room had stood there with bits of waste hanging from their pockets. The deck-hands had stood round in worn jerseys and baggy trousers. They had all listened carefully with defiance in their eyes.

Perhaps that was why the instructor had not told them the whole truth straightaway, had not been able to bring himself to tell them that the gun they regarded as their saviour was in fact a four-inch gun from the Russo-Japanese war of 1905.

The Carpenter remembered, too, what AB had said. AB was his best friend and had been invited to help clean the breach mechanism the day the gun arrived. Carefully they had carried it down to AB's berth and got a clean sheet to put the bits on it. They wanted to be sure the firing-pin worked smoothly and easily when it had to strike the detonator and send the shell straight into the U-boat.

'Just the job!' the AB had exclaimed arrogantly. He put the little piece of metal to his lips and chanted: 'May it send the shells into U-boats so that they burst asunder, so that

Germans yell and sink and drown and shut their bloody mouths.'

The Carpenter remembered he had said 'Amen' to that, and that evening they had got rather tight and merry ashore . . .

It was the second night since the attack began and those on watch were lying on the floor in the mess and galley. No one wanted to be below in their berths. If a torpedo hit your ship and you had to rush up on to the boat-deck, a delay of even a few seconds could make all the difference.

'Rush to the boat-deck, indeed,' the AB thought, as he lay on the floor in the galley, and all at once he began to laugh hysterically. Bo'sun sat up to be ready to fling himself at AB if he became violent or tried to run out on deck to jump overboard. AB laughed and laughed; then he gave a sudden sob and his laugh became shrill. There were no other sounds but that dreadful laugh and the hum of the engines while the others lying huddled round him waited with muscles tensed to deal with him the moment his mind snapped.

But the laughter stopped as abruptly as it had begun, and breathing rather heavily AB said: 'Here we are lying in the galley; but hell, it doesn't matter where one is when there's thousands of tons of explosives and nitro-glycerine below deck.'

'Shut up, will you!' Bo'sun said furiously.

Then the Greaser, the eternal grumbler, raised himself up on his elbow and staring fiercely through the dark towards the Bo'sun's berth hissed: 'Shut up yourself! We saw that ammunition ship this afternoon. One bang, a lot of flame and a cloud of smoke. Felt the heat of it even here. Not a soul was saved, not a boat or a raft got into the water. Everything blown sky high in a second!'

'Shut up, will you!' Bo'sun shouted.

Those on deck or on the bridge were still trying to keep their eyes off the port lifeboat, where the Second Mate was still sitting motionless.

Everyone was waiting for the look-out to call out, waiting to hear the sound of an explosion. Those still capable of thinking beyond what might happen the next second – before they had time to take another pull at their cigarettes – were hoping desperately that *Anna* might survive until the morning of the ninth day.

The darkness of night made it all worse. There was no chance of catching sight of a periscope or torpedo track, no chance to manœuvre or to use their gun, no chance to do anything before the ship's side was torn open and everything went sky high and then down, down into the endless depths where nineteen ships and hundreds of men of that convoy had gone already in the last two days.

Bo'sun began thinking of the currents deep down and made a desperate attempt to switch his thoughts to his favourite bar in Liverpool and all the spirits and beer he was going to drink if he survived. He could hear men breathing heavily and nervously in the darkness round him, and he wished someone would say something, anything, as long as someone just spoke. For those currents were sweeping him out of thoughts of dying and into even worse terrors, filling his mind with visions of enormous dimensions. In these the main part was played by his own dead body. The only thing visible was his lifeless body floating in the currents hundreds of fathoms down drifting in an everlasting green-black darkness, round and round eternally in the same circle, in the cold currents at depths where no living creature had ever been and to which only the drifting dead could come.

The Bo'sun now cursed himself for having told AB to shut up. If only he could find the right words now to start AB talking about the brown-eyed girl and the woman with the long black hair – the two he had left behind at home and of whom he was always ready to talk.

Perhaps his tone had been more brutal than he had meant,

just because it was AB who had lain there in the dark gasping with laughter and speaking the truth about what they could expect with a cargo of ammunition in the holds.

Almost always when AB said something it made life seem less dangerous and more hopeful. He had sparse fair hair, and in his eyes there was a mixture of sadness and friendliness that the men in *Anna* found made them less harsh and caustic in what they said whenever he was around.

His height was a little above average and he was rather narrow-shouldered, with a big head that always hung forward as if too heavy for his thin neck. When he talked with you, his head still hung in that rather woeful position, but he had a way of raising his eyebrows that made his gaze so open and frank you thought you could see right into his heart.

They often laughed at what he said. Not because he was so funny, but in the way one laughs at the chatter of the young. It was kindly, encouraging laughter. He obviously liked it, and they responded. It was enough for him to stick his tongue in the big gap between his front teeth and make a noise like the wailing of destroyers. They would have been furious with anyone else who imitated the alarm sirens, but anything AB did was innocent, harmless fun. They knew everything about him, or so they thought . . .

On all sorts of occasions while at sea or in bars ashore he had described to them his home and his wife. She had long, black hair and had been pregnant when he had gone back to sea in January 1940. They knew her favourite dishes, the tunes she hummed and the way she did her hair in front of the mirror in the kitchen in the morning. Often, in the bar or the mess, AB had tied a cloth round his waist and demonstrated the way she walked with a slight swing of her hips. He had made his hand describe curves over his own skinny figure – promising lovely curves over chest and thighs. If there was a girl in the bar with pretty brown eyes, AB would stand round after round of drinks if she would just sit with him while he explained that it was just her kind of eyes that his wife and their girl had.

Isolated aboard a ship for weeks at a time, knowing that death could strike before *Anna* rose to the next wave, the men often felt an intense need of a woman. They therefore enjoyed indulging in fantasies of AB's wife with the brown eyes and long black hair and the lovely curves AB's hands described through the cigarette smoke of the mess. But they would have bitten off their tongues rather than tell AB that they lusted after his wife. It was inconceivable that they should have discussed her in the coarse language they used to talk about girls they picked up in bars. They knew that AB must have her to himself, that she could only inhabit their dreams if they let AB dream about her aloud and no one attempted verbal rape. Anyone who was in a bad mood and felt tempted to shatter AB's dream world of innocence and beauty back in Norway still kept his mouth shut – even if he was tight. He knew that the others would never forget or forgive anyone who destroyed AB's heaven on earth.

Not even the quarrelsome, gruff Greaser had ever said anything frivolous or coarse about AB's wife. They had come to depend on the AB's fantasies. These made reality less cruel, and so they encouraged him to tell them more, were greedy for details. So AB told and described until in the end they seemed to know every vein in her body: they knew how she looked when asleep, in her nightie, how she looked bending over the baby's cot or hanging up washing outside the little house. When he was really inspired, AB could even make them smell the smell of her.

But even so it was not AB's young wife with her brown eyes and black hair that occupied their minds most. They saw women and, if they wanted, had women in their hectic hours ashore. What they liked best to hear about and talk about was AB's child. Not to begin with – not in the first few weeks after *Anna* was put on convoy work. But as time went on, they listened with mounting interest to his stories about his little girl.

AB could not know whether his wife had produced a boy or girl, did not know whether she was still alive or if the baby had ever been born. Like the other members of *Anna*'s crew he had had no news from home since the day the ship had altered course and headed for a port of which the Germans were not in control. But where the others were concerned there was never any doubt that he was the father of a baby girl with chestnut hair and brown eyes. In convoy after convoy he had told them how he was going to look after her and bring her up; and in the mess and on deck he had trundled her pram through the village street.

When half-tight in a bar he could start lulling the child to sleep, and if anyone came up to him for a brief chat, while he was 'look-out', he might tell him about the teddy bear and the dolls she was to have, had had, was to have . . .

Past and future gradually became confused, until the others no longer cared what was fantasy and what real. Their only worry was that one day AB might stop telling them, let his heavy great head sink on to his chest and fall silent, leaving them with just naked fears when afloat and drunkenness ashore and almost nothing else.

They had discovered that if they listened to him without thinking whether what he was telling was true or not, they too could see the child, see her and the garden and the village street and the teddy bear and the cot, instead of just the endless sea, the long lines of grey ships, the hunting corvettes and destroyers and the same monotonous horizon – the exploding ships and sinking ships and men burning and shrieking and drowning.

At sea, if the AB was on watch and they were tired of the tales of what they had done in this port or that, which all seemed the same, they would sit in the mess impatiently waiting for AB to come. They would sit on even when exhausted from lack of sleep, hoping for AB's child to toddle into their minds and so perhaps give them an hour or two of sleep before going on watch again. Often the stories were ones they had heard before, but every now and again AB produced something quite new.

As a rule he began by saying that the girl and he were going to do something or other, but always it was something full of sunshine and high expectations. And the moment he had got going, he and the girl were *doing* it. And whatever the two of them were at was done yesterday or this morning or they were going to do it tomorrow. And they all listened, accepted it all and laughed with him, and if he groped for a word they made encouraging suggestions and asked flattering questions.

One day when he was telling them that he was going to take his skipper's certificate and send the girl to high school, the Boy interrupted: 'But you said you would have her and your wife aboard with you when you got a ship,' he said.

The both deck-hands and engine-room hands were all in the mess and they all stared at AB. The Boy became anxious when he saw AB's head sinking lower than usual, until his chin was resting on his khaki shirt, and he sat silent, thinking. But they breathed again when he raised his eyebrows and they saw that his gaze was so distant that he must be seeing the two of them there at home.

Then AB drank the remains of his coffee and said confidently, 'We'll find a solution.'

The next day the Carpenter had found a solution. 'What about a correspondence school? Some are so good you could study to be a professor.' He pressed his lips together, pulled down the corners of his mouth and looked importantly round at the others in the mess.

They all nodded approval. AB's eyebrows had gone up so far that his forehead was covered with wrinkles. The rest of that watch below was spent discussing all the wonderful possibilities of education by correspondence course.

There was no longer any problem in having the girl aboard and at the same time seeing that she had a good education. Once he had taken his navigator's exam, AB would be able to help her with mathematics, and he was pretty good at English too. But she was still only a baby and the others could say to him good-naturedly, 'You're crazy. You mustn't give her too much chocolate and so many toys!' When they said that he would reply that kiddies ought to have a few treats, and then one of the others would begin talking about the meagreness of his own childhood in this respect, and another watch would have passed in talk that smothered their fear of torpedoes.

If the talk happened to turn on the Occupation and the danger that the Germans might rape the women there at home, AB would say that, beautiful and tempting though his wife was, she would be left alone because the Huns had this Aryan nonsense on the brain and were only interested in women with fair hair and blue eyes. But any doubts as to his child's health made him beside himself with fear and fury.

Many went like that while on the binge ashore or after weeks of great strain at sea, but it had a sinister effect on the others when AB flung his great head back and yelled that if the Germans did anything to his baby he would kill them. Kill the entire nation, after the war was over, go on killing and killing until there were not any left to kill.

The Carpenter knew how to deal with these situations. He flung his strong arms round AB and, holding him firmly, said in a quiet, kindly voice, 'Now you must go back home to your wife and brown-eyed baby and get to bed.' And AB's head would drop forward again and, back aboard *Anna*, he would take off his shoes and walk in stockinged feet to his berth so as not to wake the family.

On the rare occasions when he went with a girl to a cheap hotel, staggering and so drunk he scarcely knew what he was doing, he would be weighed to the ground with remorse all the next day. He would run to the Carpenter, his best friend, and reproach him for not keeping him away from other women.

'What would my little girl have said if she had seen me last night?' he would say plaintively.

But on this second night after U-boat attacks began, after his hysterical outburst, AB remained silent. Everyone knew that what he had said was true, but no one should have put it into words.

AB was still silent when he got up off the galley floor to take his trick at the wheel. Without stumbling or groping he made his way across the blacked-out deck and up the ladder to relieve the Boy.

He took a hard grip of the spokes. They felt damp and it struck him that the Boy's hands must have sweated a lot. He strained his eyes so that he did not lose sight of the big grey shadow of the ship ahead with which *Anna* had to keep in line. If a ship lost its place in the convoy, the others might all be thrown off course, and collision might lead to sinking or to damage so bad that one of the ships would be left behind, a cripple among a lot of murderers.

When he had been staring so long that the shadow of the ship in front began to merge with the darkness, AB shifted his gaze to the wake of the ship *Anna* was following. When it was calm, the swirling white foam above the propellers was like a glint of silver on the black surface of the water.

So AB steered and waited for the torpedo to hit them. The Skipper paced to and fro across the bridge, expecting to be torpedoed. The First Mate in the chart-house was expecting to be torpedoed, as were Bo'sun and the others lying on the floor in galley and mess, Donkeyman in the engine-room, the Chief and the Boy, Steward and Cook and the nerve-shocked No. 2 on the thwart of the swung-out port lifeboat. All of them lay awake waiting for a torpedo to strike . . .

In the east, dawn appeared in the black wall between heaven and sea, and hundreds of men in the convoy looked out across the waters with bloodshot eyes. Another day of staring search for periscope and torpedo track had begun. They grey twilight made their faces even greyer. Their mouths felt leathery and stinking. Their throats were raw after all the cigarettes they had smoked. They hawked and coughed, some of them so violently that their faces flushed crimson as they leaned over the rail or bulwark to spit, their whole bodies aching with lack of sleep and tension.

The first grey light was followed by a brighter light and morning of their tenth day out had dawned.

They kept staring for trails of bubbles, expecting every moment the ear-splitting bang when they would be blown to smithereens. The deck-hand, whom they all called the Boy because he looked so young and childish, sat on the boat-deck calculating how many days he had lived. It was seventeen times three hundred and sixty-five plus six months and two weeks. He made it that he had lived for six thousand three hundred and ninety-nine days. He looked up at the port lifeboat, where the Second Mate sat on the thwart, dumb and motionless at the start of his second day there. If I see him there tomorrow, the Boy thought, I shall have lived for six thousand four hundred days exactly.

He must work out how many hours he had lived, too. If he lived until the next day, it would be a pretty big figure. He worked it out on the back of a packet of cigarettes and made it one hundred and fifty-three thousand six hundred hours exactly.

On this day the U-boats did not return to the attack in the early morning as they had on the two previous days. The seventeen ships still afloat steamed on their way towards the British Isles and midday came without anything happening. By mid-afternoon not a ship had been sunk all that day and the Boy calculated that if he was alive at the same time the following day, he would then have been alive for one hundred and fifty-three thousand six hundred and seven hours.

The Boy was not much more than five foot six. He had curly hair and when he went ashore he used quantities of greasy hair lotion to make it lie flat with a parting at the side. He wished he could achieve the Bo'sun's neat flat head. He often walked with raised shoulders and arms held a little way out from his body because that made him feel taller and stronger.

All his shoes had leather heels. It gave him confidence to hear his heels click against the deck, pavement, or floor of the bar. When he remembered to do so, he would bring his feet down hard, almost stamping, and in a narrow street his footsteps echoed between the walls and he thought that anyone hearing them must think they were those of a strong man who was afraid of nothing. He cursed and swore whenever he opened his mouth, feeling that he must do that if he was really to be one of them; he used long strings of oaths, the worst he knew, mostly copied from Greaser who snapped them out at people. They were all about God and the devil and Christ, and when he made use of one of these Greaser's specials he always felt slightly apprehensive of punishment from on high, and his tongue felt stiff and numb. His grandmother had always said that if you took God's name in vain you could be struck dumb.

The Boy never swore if the Chief was within earshot. The Chief believed that there was a God in heaven. And once long before, when the U-boats had been just as numerous and murderous as on this convoy, the Chief had patted the Boy's curly head and said, 'It will be all right.' And that afternoon when a tanker had gone up in flames just beside *Anna*, the

Chief had come over to the Boy with a couple of shirts and said, 'You can have these.'

The Carpenter, hurrying past across the boat-deck, called: 'Hallo, Boy!' The seventeen-year-old returned a very grown-up greeting and pulled out a cigarette in irritation at still being called Boy. That was right as long as he really was ship's boy, though he would have preferred to have been called 'Deckie', but now that he was a deck-hand he felt he deserved something better than 'Boy'.

'Boy-Boy-Boy!' he said to himself in a low voice, banging his fist angrily against the lifeboat at each 'Boy'. He raised his shoulders and said aloud: 'To hell with that!' He had been in a ship that was blown up between Iceland and Scotland in the summer of 1940.

It was a ship of 1500 tons laden with fish. Two German planes unloaded their bombs on her. He saw the bombs growing bigger and bigger, then the explosion had come and he was flung up and up and up; then down and down; and an orange film had been over his eyes and heat had scorched his face. All round him there was a confusion of coils of wire and iron plates and then the whole of the sea had come foaming in over the boat.

It was as if the boat went to pieces under him and then everything had gone dark. He had seen his mother with her arms stretched out towards him and again and again he tried to take hold of her hands. And then his head had cleared and he saw that he was banging his fist into the water.

He was not wearing a life-jacket, but he found a large piece of hatch and climbed on to it and sat there with legs dangling over the edge. He had heard someone shouting and recognized the voice as the captain's. Otherwise it would have been difficult to see who it was, for blood from his crown and forehead was pouring over his face; but it was the captain all right calling orders to men he could neither see nor hear.

The pouring blood was like a red curtain in front of the Boy's eyes and even if it was partially washed away when a wave rolled over his injured head, it was there again the moment his head was free of the water.

'Get away from the propeller. Away from the boat!' the captain shouted, and now, if the Boy had a bad night, he could still hear those shouts.

He was fifteen at the time. He paddled with his hands and kicked with his feet and reached the captain. He then saw that his head had been split open from crown to the root of his nose, and in the gap was what looked like brain. He took hold of the captain's arms, shut his eyes, and was pulled up on to the hatch.

Then he got up on to another piece of wreckage, cries sounding all round him. He saw a sailor splashing with one arm while holding up the stump of the other. It had been shorn through just below the elbow and blood was spurting from the stump which kept going under and emerging again. The Boy thought he was going out of his mind. The shrieks from the sailor with the stump were like fiery claws in his head, and if they stopped momentarily because the man's mouth was full of water, there were the screams of the others elsewhere.

Then the Boy had been pulled on to a raft by the strong arms of one of the mates. There were only the two of them on the raft; then they pulled up a third, one of the engine-room crew. He had not a stitch on. All his clothes had been blown off him when the boiler exploded, and the mate said he must have been flung through a hole in the ship's side.

The man's gaze was fixed and blood trickled from his nose and ears. He had talked incessantly during the short time he was on the raft. It was a small raft and there was no room to struggle and restrain him when he insisted on getting back into the water.

The Boy and the mate were found by a British trawler.

They were given dry clothes and food and whisky. The war had not been going very long then and the trawler set course for where the mate thought his ship had been bombed. The trawler was only just out from her home port in Shetland and had a vaseful of flowers on board – with these and a bit of wire and a couple of signal flags cut into strips they made something that resembled a wreath.

When they thought they had reached the place where the Norwegian boat had gone down, they stopped the engines and the mate had stood by the rail and said:

'You will never return home, but we shall remember you as long as we live. Peace be on your memory and thanks for everything . . .'

The crew of the trawler had stood round and they had all looked at the water as the wreath fell on to it. All the time this was being done, in his mind's eye the Boy saw the thin figure of the captain and heard him shouting, 'Get away from the propellers. Away from the ship.' And the Boy leaned over the rail and bowed deeply to the wreath that he could still see on the crest of the waves.

That was all a long time ago. He had been in *Anna* over two years now. And they still called him the Boy!

It was their tenth day out from New York. The Boy went up on to the bridge to take his trick at the wheel.

Anna was still afloat on the fourth day of the U-boat attack. The sea was still calm, and some of the men tried the old dodge of provoking the weather gods. A good strong wind and heavy seas made it more difficult for the U-boats to operate, and the men would rather have had a hurricane to deal with than an invisible enemy, for whose purposes good weather was ideal.

Light cloud hung above the heavily laden ships, now half-way across the Atlantic.

The U-boats failed to attack at their usual time, in the grey hours. Nine o'clock came and then eleven and then twelve without a ship having been sunk. Some of the men were even beginning to hope that the pack might have given up the chase. By mid-afternoon quite a lot of them were hoping that perhaps the U-boats had used up all their torpedoes and gone back to port to replenish their magazines and to refuel. *Anna*'s Bo'sun began to think that there was a chance of his getting tight once again.

The quiet persisted until dusk was falling, but then an ammunition ship to starboard of *Anna* went sky high. Pillars of orange flame reared into the air with hundreds of crackling flashes of lightning. Dark bits of ship's side and deck and hatch swirled through flames high above the surface. Then came a wave of heat, a jagged wall of smoke and, when the wind had blown it aside, nothing, nothing on the surface, nothing in the air.

The ship had exploded so close to *Anna* that the blast had made her heel over, sending pots and pans, knives and forks hurtling to the floor in galley and mess. Open doors shut with a bang and closed doors flew open; the deck cargo creaked in its lashings and the Skipper on the bridge lost his balance and banged his head against the rail.

Someone on the poop called out 'We've been torpedoed!' and those in the stern made a dash for the boat-deck. People came running from all sides, making for the lifeboats and rafts. But the engines worked on steadily and the stem ploughed through the green-grey sea as before, and men who found themselves on the boat-deck, chests heaving after that wild rush across the decks and up ladders, might have felt a bit ashamed of giving way to panic if they had had time even to look at each other. But there was great hurry to rescue the starboard lifeboat which was dangling with its bows pointing at the water.

The Cook had been sitting beside this lifeboat when the blast from the exploding ammunition ship made *Anna* heel over. He had made a desperate attempt to lower the lifeboat by himself, but in his panic he had forgotten to take a turn of the fall round a bitt, so that when the lifeboat's stern dived almost vertically at the water he had to cling to the fall in an attempt to hold it back. The rope just ran through his hands, flaying the skin off his fingers and palms.

While the others were getting the lifeboat back into place the Cook stood gasping in agony; then he turned his bloody palms towards the bows for the wind to cool them and ease the pain.

This gave the men an excuse to forget their own panic and talk of the lifeboat and the Cook's injured hands instead. Being the Cook he got perhaps more sympathy than another would have done.

The helmsman held on to the spokes of the wheel and so managed to remain standing. He never let go. Now he saw the Skipper laboriously getting to his feet. First he got on to his knees, hands groping for the rail; then, having got hold of the rail, he dragged himself upright. He put his right hand to his head and fingered it cautiously. When he looked at his fingers again, they were flecked with blood. His ears ached and he felt giddy, but turning to the helmsman he said curtly: 'It's only a scratch.'

The Skipper stayed on the bridge as long as the attack lasted and for another hour after the last boat was hit.

When peace returned to the sea and the convoy on that tenth day out, there were thirteen ships left of the original thirty-six.

That evening they made contact with the shocked Second Mate. The Skipper had kept an eye on him all the time and every now and then had gone up and spoken to him in a friendly tone, but until now the man on the thwart had neither moved nor spoken. Now the Skipper had paid him another visit and, seeing that the blanket they had placed over the mate's knees had slipped off and was lying on the floor boards, he bent down and replaced it round the man's knees. Glancing up he saw that the Second Mate's eyes were no longer fixed and staring. The pupils moved. As the eyes saw the bandage on the Skipper's head with its patches of red, all at once life came back into his face; then the Mate let his head sink, and his shoulders shook with sobs.

The Skipper glanced round; then he laid his hand gently on the other's man shoulder, pressing it against the quivering muscle as if wanting to communicate warmth and comfort to the man's tortured mind. In a low voice he said: 'We're all pretty much at the end of our tether.' Then he took a firm grip of the Second Mate's upper arm and helped him off the thwart, out of the boat and into the sick-bay.

On the eleventh day the alarm sounded just after noon.

Most of the men in *Anna* had given up hoping. They could not expect to be spared much longer. The U-boats had been going for the biggest boats since the start of the attack and *Anna* was one of the largest of the thirteen still afloat.

A smaller boat, which was quite fast and which had the job of fishing survivors out of the water, still survived. The Carpenter and AB were standing in the poop looking astern at the rescue-boat, which reminded them of the coastal mail boats at home. Strange that she's survived so long, the Carpenter thought. Time after time these last few days she had had to reduce speed and then stop for minutes at a time, while survivors were pulled straight out of the water or life-boat, minutes during which she was a sitting target for a U-boat.

As though he had read the Carpenter's thoughts, AB remarked that the only explanation was that the corvettes had been circling round the rescue-boat dropping protective chains of depth-charges.

'If they've been collecting people off all the boats that have gone down already, there must be a hell of a lot of people in the rescue-boat now,' AB said.

They went on talking about the rescue-boat and so actually had their eyes on her when the torpedo hit her.

She did not sink at once, but lay more or less horizontal with a grey-white blanket of smoke and steam amidships. Through his glasses the Skipper saw lifeboats and rafts in the water. Some of them were clear of the ship's side when a second explosion splintered the forepart and the rescue-boat began to settle by the bows.

The two corvettes hurled themselves towards the sinking ship. One had climbing-nets hanging like coarse-meshed seine from her deck to the water's edge. The other hunted round dropping depth-charges to keep the U-boats away if that were possible. The nets were quickly studded with climbing figures, and men were being hauled in over the rail. It was all done at speed, but fast as the practised naval ratings did their jobs saving as many of the hundred or more in the water as could get to the corvette's side, their ship lay motionless just a few seconds too long.

The torpedo sped past just below men floating in their life-jackets and struck the side where the climbing-nets were fullest of panting, gasping men, reaching for the deck and what they had thought was safety. They were killed, and so were many of those who had already got aboard. Those who had stayed midships or aft and were left conscious and able to move, rushed round looking for another means of rescue.

Anna's Donkeyman wished for a sea of gin to dull his nerves. When he was not thinking about drink, he was praying to God. Praying was a thing he had not done since he was a little boy and he could not remember much even of the Lord's Prayer, but he thought it would be all right if he just repeated 'Help me, God – help me, God!' hour after hour.

He had been at his post in the engine-room below deck and so had seen nothing, and that was the most dreadful thing of all to have to stay there as in a trap and hear the explosions above water and the number of depth-charges going off deep below, each like a great fist banging on the ship's bottom.

At times Donkeyman's hand trembled so violently that it was almost impossible to guide his grease-gun. As he prayed 'Help me, God' to himself, his mouth was half open, because he was continually on the point of calling up to those on deck to ask what was happening. But when you were in the engine-room you did not call out however many explosions there were, and so he had swallowed the words and sweated and prayed and gripped on to something because his legs were half-paralysed with fear.

Donkeyman was twenty-eight, but he felt worn-out and aged. Lack of sleep and tension had given him an aching ring round his head, and inside his brain fear swirled like mist making it impossible for him to think clearly or coherently. He stood looking at the ladder that led up to the deck, to the light and the fresh air – the shortest way to the lifeboats and the rafts.

The violent explosions had given him an all but uncontrollable urge to rush up on deck and fling himself overboard, away from it all, into the deep.

The Greaser had several times rushed up the ladder saying he would stand at the top and give a shout if anything struck *Anna*. As if there was any point in calling at all if a ship with a cargo of ammunition was struck, Donkeyman thought. But he had not jeered at Greaser, just said 'All right.'

The Chief had been on deck when the rescue-boat and the corvette were hit. He was getting on for sixty and religious but, as the Bo'sun said, was prepared to let others have their disbelief if it made them happy. The men liked him because he did his job and tried to be nice to everybody. With folded hands he had watched from the after deck the sinking boats and the dying men and those fighting for life in the sea. Then he had gone below once more. The others had not reacted when they saw him down there again, even though it was not his watch. He was almost always in the engine-room, except when he was asleep.

The Chief had grey tousled hair, a stoop, and baggy dungarees which made him look big-bottomed. He always spoke slowly and was rather long-winded. Now he turned his gentle, short-sighted eyes on Donkeyman and said, 'I can manage by myself here for a bit, so for the time being you can go on deck . . .'

Greaser was already on his way up the ladder. Being in the belly of the ship made him feel like a blind man. All day he had been staring and staring at the ship's side. He had got it into his head that the torpedo's warhead with its charge of explosives was going to penetrate into the engine-room and hit him in the stomach and explode with him draped over it. But Donkeyman stood where he was, and all at once he felt stronger because he had done so and he said:

'If you are to be here, I can see my watch out.'

Donkeyman could not see whether the Chief approved or not. The Chief was an old man. Whatever the reason, Donkeyman suddenly found himself thinking of the last Christmas Eve aboard *Anna*. They were in an Atlantic convoy then too, and ships were going down, though not so many as now. All that day they were left in peace and that night they were all in the mess eating Christmas fare and drinking the traditional tot – all, that is, except one of the deck-hands, who spent the night sitting on the boat deck because he could not get his fear of torpedoes under control. The Skipper came in to wish them a Merry Christmas and they were amazed when, glancing at the well-laden table, he had told them that the ham had stuck in his throat. He had not been able to get any of it down because he had been thinking of those at home in Norway, and of their need.

The surly old Greaser had scowled at the Skipper and said: 'It won't make them any less hungry if we do without.'

'Perfectly true,' the Skipper replied, and each man decided that he would beat the Greaser up if they reached port alive. It had seemed so strangely solemn of the Skipper to say that he had not been able to eat for thinking of those in need at home. It was so utterly unlike him to say anything about his own feelings. He only spoke of what concerned the ship and her crew, and if the talk turned on the war he usually said: 'We must go on sailing until it's over,' and there was little else he ever said even on that subject.

They had no contact with Norway, did not know whether wives, children, friends, brothers and sisters were alive. It must have been the Chief's readiness to let them go up on deck that had made Donkeyman suddenly think of Christmas. They were sitting in the mess then eating their Christmas dinner and talking about this and that. But it was more difficult than usual for them to control their thoughts. Frequently whoever was speaking would stop in the middle of a sentence and the one who was being spoken to never heard what was said or saw what was happening round about him. They tossed down the tots poured out for them. They talked about Christmas trees and presents and, not having either on board because of the war, they spoke of them as being rather silly and joked about them – because unless you could make a joke of what you missed – or feared – most, it was best to keep silent.

'What do we want with presents?' Bo'sun said. 'We have to live the way the landlubbers see us, "tough guys" who sail in ships and drink and whore.'

It was that moment the Chief appeared with a number of little parcels. There had been one for each of them, and each had his name written on the paper. The Chief stood there in the mess cleaning his strong spectacles, which magnified his near-sighted gentle eyes so that it was like looking through the glass at a couple of blue pools. He had on a dark blue suit he had bought off the peg in Norway when he happened to be home on leave at the time his first-born was baptized.

That was so long ago that his son was himself in a ship in a convoy now, but the suit was spotless and with his thin grey hair beautifully brushed, and those spectacles, he looked rather like an important businessman.

The Chief said that they must not misunderstand him, what was in the parcels was not really worth having, but this was Christmas and these were tokens to remind them of presents.

They unwrapped the parcels – some did so slowly and deliberately to prolong the excitement as far as possible; others just snapped the pretty red string. They all had the same: four hazel nuts. The Chief must have been saving them in his cabin since the last pre-war Christmas.

They looked at the nuts solemnly. Some left them on the table beside their plates; others carefully packed them again and put them in their pockets.

'Yes, well, thanks very much, Chief,' Bo'sun said, and the others muttered assent, while the Chief went on polishing his spectacles. 'Even tough guys can appreciate a present at Christmas,' Bo'sun added, and the others nodded agreement. No one laughed. They just nodded agreement.

They had lumps in their throats. They knew that the Chief was religious and that Christmas meant a lot to him, and at that moment they thought him not just a decent chap but a devilish good one.

Donkeyman remembered all this as he stood at his post in the engine-room, but the sudden explosion of yet another depth-charge brought his thoughts back to the present. Things must be worse than ever, he thought, if the Chief was allowing them all up on deck saying he could manage alone for a while. But nonetheless Donkeyman felt slightly less afraid than he had been earlier in the day. Having the Chief down there with him somehow made it easier to breathe.

Then darkness fell over the sea for the eleventh time since the convoy left New York. The Boy was at the wheel.

Exhausted and dizzy he just hung on the spokes. He had not had one full hour's sleep since the U-boat attacks began. He had kept his watches and otherwise been in the mess or sat on the boat deck with his back against the funnel, eyes searching for torpedo tracks by day and at night just waiting for the explosion.

The slightest sound was like an electric shock in his head and body. He dozed at times, dropping off for a few minutes, but fear was always there making proper sleep impossible. Standing there with straddled legs, red-rimmed eyes staring at the looming dark shape of the ship ahead of *Anna*, he was glad of the support of the wheel.

When they were in port, as they had just been in New York, there was plenty of opportunity for sleep, but in sleep he so often relived the bombing of the fishing-boat in the summer of 1940, saw the skipper's split-open head and heard him shouting 'Get away from the propeller! Get away from the ship!' and that made him cry, half-stifled cries as he struggled free of sleep and its nightmare.

Mile after mile the convoy ploughed its way towards Britain, a flock of huge shadows in the night. All lights were carefully covered: ventilators, doorways, hatches, even the compass was almost blacked out. The binnacle was so well covered that there was only a faint yellow glow on the compass rose and the arrow that showed the course for England.

There were ten ships left now and the men in them were worn by lack of sleep and constant fear. Not one of them had taken his clothes off since the journey began. They all wore their life-jackets the whole time. They scarcely ate because they had no appetite, and when they did they could not have told you what they were eating. Few of them spoke, and when someone did he could hardly recognize his own voice.

If they peered out into the darkness, it was to see something darker than the night: the ship on the beam in the port or starboard column.

It was autumn, and they shivered. They knew they could see or know nothing until the torpedo struck, if it was going to, yet they still stared at the sea. A U-boat might have been just a few yards away with its periscope up, and they would never have seen the thin tube with the curve at the end like a snake's head ready to strike – the U-boat's evil eye, which enabled the German sailors to follow the convoy however quiet the ships in it were.

Hour after hour the men waited. By night they might as well have been blind. They could see nothing and do nothing to help themselves. Trapped.

Their whole world was the distance between stem and stern. They had nowhere to run. They had to stay aboard; and whether they were in the bows, on the poop or amidships, on the bridge or in the engine-room, they were equally doomed if a torpedo hit the ship. Whether their deeds had been good or evil, whether they believed in God or not, whether they loved life or hated it, whether they had ten children or no family at all, irrespective of what they were or were not, what they had done or not done with their lives, they would all be blown to pieces if a torpedo struck them.

Anna's Cook was sitting with bandaged hands on the boat deck. He wanted to shout his fears out aloud, but he was so afraid that a torpedo was going to strike before he could get a sound out that his fear stifled the cry in his throat. He saw his severed right arm being flung through a thundering storm of fire high into the night sky, and the white-bandaged hand on it waved to his left leg as it sped across the water and fell on the deck of the ship ahead of them. All this he saw with his left eye that the explosion had forced out of its socket and was floating high up above and then fell into the open mouth of a fish on the surface – a fish that had been lying there a long time waiting for it.

Then a cry did come from the Cook. It was neither loud

nor penetrating, more a howl from a distant boat. He fell over backwards.

The next moment the Bo'sun was there, shaking the Cook and talking to him. But the Cook was unconscious. His breathing was laboured and irregular. The Bo'sun peeled off his life-jacket and placed it under the Cook's head. When that was done, day was only a few minutes away. The stars had paled in the blue-black sky, and the outlines of the other ships in the convoy had become much sharper and were now grey against the reddening horizon. So the Cook was taken down to his berth and Bo'sun sat beside him to keep watch.

Men stretched stiff limbs, had a smoke, turned grimy, stubbly faces to the rising sun, narrowed their eyes against the sharp light, ran a comb or their fingers through their hair, and went to the mess for a mug of coffee.

Ten o'clock came, then twelve, then two and then four without a ship going down. All that afternoon, evening and night the convoy continued on its way unhindered. All the following day there was not a sign of a U-boat either, and again some began to hope the pack had let go of them.

The Skipper had been on the bridge for more than six days and nights. He had been at his post ever since the attack began. He had spent most of the first few days pacing to and fro, but later he had stood, leaning against the rail or bulkhead, without which he could scarcely have remained on his feet.

Now and again he would stagger into the chart-house and sit down on the worn black leather seat in the tiny space of the wheelhouse; but it was only for minutes at a time and soon he had staggered out again and once more was staring to starboard, port, for'ard and astern. His head swam and his eyes ached. Now and again came a surge of pain so intense that he could scarcely see as far as the bows. He realized that he must look ghastly, for every man who came to relieve the helmsman gave him a horrified look: it was his eyes, so shot with blood that the blue pupils were surrounded by an orange-coloured mass. Every sound seemed to come to him from afar and when at long intervals he spoke a word or two to the man at the wheel or the officer of the watch his own voice sounded remote.

The ten ships were left to sail on in peace for another day and a night, and on the third night after the sinkings stopped most men had ventured down to their cabins. Some could not bring themselves to lie in their bunks. You could lose valuable seconds in getting out, so they lay on the deck instead, their life-jackets cushioning them against the hardness. They hooked the door back so that it stood open and some even wedged it with a piece of wood so that they were sure it would not slam shut and perhaps be impossible to open, if the ship were struck.

Almost all lay down in their clothes, and if they did not have their life-jackets on they kept them always within reach, ever ready to leap out of their cabin, out of the mess, wheel-house, galley or engine-room – ready to make a dash for life-boat or raft, bulwark or sea.

Most of them managed to keep their fear under control. When there was not an alert, they sat in the mess seemingly calm, or lay in their cabins trying to sleep, or did their work as a matter of course however nervous and exhausted they felt. During the short hectic time they spent ashore some of them had adopted such a devil-may-care attitude that few land-lubbers could realize what they were going through now.

If the men could not keep their mortal fear under control, the ship would soon become a floating bedlam. It was the unwritten, but most important law of all that each must hide his fears, endure his terror alone. No one must try to diminish his fear by displaying it and thereby making others' fear more difficult to bear. If you could not speak with hatred or scorn of what threatened you, then you should keep silent. And if someone was unable to endure this inhuman pressure, no one must mock him, if only because any one of them might lose his own self-control before the hour was out. This unwritten law was observed so scrupulously that even the most tormented did not break it. This was why one so seldom noticed any transition from normal behaviour to total collapse. The mental breakdown came with the suddenness of the torpedo, and a man had flung himself overboard before anyone could put out a hand to stop him.

There was nothing unusual in one or two more venturing to go into their cabins at night, instead of sitting or lying on the boat-deck as they did during an alert. When someone sat, back to the funnels, preoccupied with his own fears, the others would often try to cheer him up. In gratitude he could easily thaw and talk and talk, producing his best and funniest stories and, if he did not have enough of his own experiences, stealing other people's and retelling them as his – anything to retain his audiences and escape the solitude of the dark deck.

The ten ships sailed on straight for the coast of England. Another couple of days and the convoy would be in port. Already they had seen British planes overhead.

Those who did not try to sleep spent their watch below in the mess where the packs of cards were in constant use. Those who lost at poker or pontoon did not care even if they were cleaned out. The others always paid for the drinks of any who had to go ashore with empty pockets. Even the man who won pot after pot did not gather up the money with greedy hands. He knew he would not keep it long, that he might not live long enough to use any of it.

They had stopped discussing how long the war might last. No one now wagered that it would be over by the spring, summer or next autumn. No one any longer said 'When we get home to Norway . . .' They had seen so much that now they always began with '*If* we get back . . .' or 'If I should manage . . .'

The married men talked most of 'If I get back . . .', but they now spoke of their families in quite a different way. Before the war they spent hours discussing their spouses' deficiencies and merits, attractiveness and ability to budget, how clever the wife was at saving, how much she was able to do on a quid. Always there was someone to cap this, his wife getting more for even less. Now they anxiously spoke their fears that those at home probably did not have any money to buy things with, and wondered whether there was even food to be bought.

Often when they sat in the mess with a heaped plate in front of them, they would think how perhaps their wives and children were going hungry and so felt ashamed of all the food available for them. A mouthful of meat, bread or fruit could suddenly become impossible to get down, and a man would sometimes stand up and hurriedly leave the table.

They had told each other about their families, wives and children, homes and neighbours, over and over again, in the mess and in bars ashore. None of it was very interesting, just ordinary things about ordinary people. It was only AB with his brown-eyed daughter and wife with long, black hair who could go on telling tales about them without the others tiring of listening to him. AB dared to say what they wished to dream and found words for feelings that they too had, but could not express.

They forgot the difficulties they had to contend with ashore before the war, shoved aside all irksome memories of failure and disappointment, no longer remembered that you could have bad moments everywhere and that few days are entirely good no matter where you are or who you are.

For over two years now they had received no letters from home. The tendency to idealize and to yearn grew as the distance in time increased, and this yearning became painfully intense when the British or American newspapers wrote about the terror and shortages of food in the occupied countries.

One evening in the mess they were talking about the daring acts of sabotage carried out in several places in Norway, becoming excited with admiration for the Resistance men at home.

'I don't think I would have the nerve to take part in anything like that,' the Carpenter said.

The Boy had no doubts. He would have hidden in the forest several miles above the valley from which he came. Since he was a boy he had known every nook and cranny there and knew of caves and rocky shelves which no German would ever find. At night he would have made his way down to the places where Germans lived and thrown hand-grenades through the windows and then run back to his hiding place. At other times, he would have haunted the fringe of the forest with a Krag-Jørgensen, which was the best rifle in the world, shooting Germans. He would have shot them all in the head so that no one would have known exactly who had done it. And he would then have run back to the security of his mountain cave . . .

They let him chatter away, glad that someone was saying something they had not heard a thousand times before.

They talked, too, about how each of them was insured for fifteen thousand crowns which would be paid to their families if they were killed.

'There'll be a good many rich widows at home before this business is over,' Bo'sun said.

The others at the table laughed – some because they thought it amusing, others because it was one of those remarks at which one was supposed to laugh. Greaser alone sat with his usual sullen expression and drooping lip. He glowered at Bo'sun then suddenly he said angrily: 'Several hundred merry widows for damned landlubbers in the damned heap of stones we're sailing for.'

He glared round the mess challenging each of them by naming the place where his home was and adding: 'Dreadful place! Filthy hole!'

'Shut up!' Bo'sun said.

AB could not bear quarelling and he tried to save the situation by asking Greaser to 'Chuck the potatoes across.' Greaser picked up the dish of potatoes and literally threw it. It struck AB's shoulder and the potatoes went rolling across the floor.

'You get what you ask for here,' he shouted angrily. 'You and your brown-eyed chit.'

The others turned to look at AB and, beside himself with rage, Greaser took hold of another dish and turned it upside down. Meat balls rolled across the table and brown rivers of sauce spread over the wax cloth, while Greaser shouted: 'Just flour and water! What the hell does the steward think he'll do with all the meat and egg, when this damned hulk's lying on the bottom?'

Before he had finished, Carpenter was standing beside him. 'Out on deck with you!' Carpenter said, and pulling Greaser to his feet shoved him ahead of him through the door. The others followed in silence.

Carpenter gave Greaser a box on the ears and Greaser tried to hit back. He had to, yet he did not dare put any force behind the blow in case the mighty Carpenter lost his temper and really used his vast strength. Carpenter pushed Greaser backwards towards Bo'sun who gave him another box on the ear.

Greaser was still trying to bluff, pretending he was spoiling for a fight; he put his hands up in a boxing guard and straddled his legs. Then Bo'sun's right arm went out and gave Greaser a push in the direction of Donkeyman, who gave him another slap.

The wind had freshened and was sending dark clouds scudding past overhead out into the Atlantic where the pack of U-boats had savaged the convoy. The seas were dead ahead and every time they gave him a push Greaser nearly went over, but he kept on trying to make them think he was not to be intimidated.

The Boy could not strike anyone even if others could. He was standing pale-faced and uncomfortable, with hands in his trousers-pockets, when Greaser lurched towards him, so Greaser hit him instead, just to show that he was a man who gave as good as he got. Those who could hit did so even harder than they really meant, because they had had so many days in the convoy in mortal fear, defenceless.

Staggering and stumbling, Greaser wove about the deck. His head was bowed, but he still tried to keep his hands up in the attitude of boxers he had seen in photographs. And the days and nights of fearing being torpedoed found expression in the mounting anger of the men surrounding him who were beginning to feel their hatred of him in their knuckles.

'Will you behave properly in the mess?' Carpenter said.

Greaser stood swaying on his feet. His ill-tempered, drooping lip was swollen and his nose was bleeding. Just then *Anna* dug her bows into the trough of a wave and he would have fallen if AB had not caught hold of him. It was the first time AB had been near him and Greaser's reply was to strike an angry, but not very forceful blow on AB's arm. He had still not answered the Carpenter.

Anna thumped her way through a few more seas while they waited for him to reply. The anger began to ebb in those who had struck him. Now they just hoped he would give in.

The Carpenter repeated his question. Seconds passed, then they heard Greaser mutter, 'Go to hell, the lot of you!' He would rather be knocked senseless than be humbled in full view of everyone. The Carpenter hesitated, raised his fist, lowered it again; then he pressed his lips together and gave Greaser another box on the ear.

Donkeyman pulled a piece of waste from the hip pocket of his dungarees and held it out, telling Greaser to wipe off the blood that was running from his nose, but Greaser would not take it. His face smarted and there was such a roaring in his ears that the Carpenter's voice seemed to come from a loud-speaker a long way away, when for the third time he asked, 'Will you behave properly in the mess?'

They stood round him in silence, feeling so uncomfortable that they could not look at each other. They knew that they would have lost all along the line if that ragged figure once more muttered: 'Go to hell, the lot of you!' But Greaser said nothing, just stood with arms hanging at his sides, eyes fixed on the deck.

Greaser had always felt himself an outsider, in this and all other ships he had been aboard. So much did he feel this that he did not even go ashore with the others, but bought himself a bottle and sat by himself in the ship drinking and cursing until he fell asleep. He was full of bitterness, a long-standing bitterness, old and hard as granite.

His cheeks were aflame from all the slaps he had been dealt. He swallowed the blood trickling into his throat and with it something else that was suppressed tears, but he could not say 'yes' to the Carpenter. The men surrounding him felt uncomfortable and guilty.

Many of them had been involved in fights or had had at one time or another to defend themselves with their bare fists, but they were not hard enough to bear the sight of a man conquered and humbled in their own ship. But how else could they have dealt with a man who threw a dish of potatoes at another and tipped the meat on to the table? Yet they knew that this should never have happened.

Greaser was still standing, staring at the deck, and they saw that he was swallowing the lumps in his throat. But still he said nothing. And when Bo'sun broke the awkward silence by saying that he was going in for a cup of coffee, the others hurried after him and through the door into the mess like sheep.

Left alone on deck, Greaser picked up the piece of waste and held it to his nose . . .

For the first time for many days the Skipper went to his cabin to lie down. His red, swollen eyes ached after days and nights of staring from the bridge, and his head swam so that he had been afraid he would collapse before he got to his bunk.

Sleep would not come. He lay there thinking of all the things that would have to be done if *Anna* managed to reach Liverpool. He must engage shore watchmen, to give the crew the most possible free time – he knew how worn-out they were. He was continually amazed by man's capacity to endure. But there was a limit, and the time must come when they would reach the end of their physical strength and will-power.

He ought to have taken leave. He had a right to leave after more than two years' uninterrupted service. But he would not take it this time either. The Cook must be got to hospital and the Second Mate had asked to be signed off. Perhaps he ought to go and see a doctor himself in Liverpool? No. If he did, others must do so too. You did not require medical training to see that several of them were on the verge of a breakdown.

No, forget it! He needed the men in *Anna* and they were too short a time in port for any treatment to be effective.

They had to put to sea again, to sail and go on sailing until they were sunk or broke down and were sent to hospital.

As the Skipper lay in his bunk, in his mind's eye he could see the faces of a long string of men he had known and who had sailed on and on until their ships had been sent to the bottom.

His eyes burned and red wisps of mist swirled across the bulkheads and cabin roof, but he could see the faces of the dead he had known quite distinctly. He could see his own exhausted men, too, and he took comfort from the thought that he was going to hire shore watchmen so that all of the crew who wished could storm down the gangway to the nearest bar. Get beer and whisky, drink themselves into a stupor and so find sleep and oblivion.

If only he could get half an hour's sleep. He had drink in his cupboard, lots of it, but he could not drink himself into a stupor in his ship. Not even when in port. He and the mates had to see that unloading went ahead properly. Damage had to be repaired, fresh instruments and other equipment had to be procured to replace what had worn out or been broken. The ship had to be in first-class condition, or at least in the best possible shape for the next crossing.

He had to be sober and alert in case a despairing Chief came complaining that he did not have enough men to overhaul the engines, or a furious mate should appear raging that there were only two men on deck and discharging and unloading were almost at a standstill.

There were the dead men's faces again. Just above his bunk. Striped with red. They were staring down at him, and he muttered that he was going to go on sailing and would stay aboard round the clock and every day of the year, because this was his ship. He was not going to leave her, would not take leave. The authorities praised him for his zeal and sense of duty and refusal to go on leave. When they did, he remained silent, for he could not tell them the truth – could not say to their shaven, well-rested faces that it was not just a sense of duty and his desire to serve his country and the Allied cause that kept him aboard his ship. And because he said nothing and was not greedy for honours, they praised his conscientiousness and loyalty even higher.

For a long time the main reason for his never taking leave had been that he could not bear the thought of anyone else being in command of *Anna*. If he went on leave, *Anna* might be a thousand miles away by the time his leave was over and then he would be given another boat.

He knew *Anna* inside out. He knew just how much the almost twenty-year-old boat was good for, knew her strong points and her weaknesses; he knew her engines, could hear the slightest fault in any of her bearings; he was more intimate with her than with any human being.

The officers were first-class seamen – the Second Mate had known his job and been a good man to have until his breakdown. He would like to have had him stay on in *Anna*, but he had asked to be signed off. It was no use telling him that every man in *Anna*, in every ship in every convoy, could break down as he had and sit on the thwart of a swung-out lifeboat, a living corpse.

It felt as if a red-hot iron was being pressed against his eyes, but he must not give in to the pain and his tiredness, which was torture. And he must get rid of the faces of those who had gone down. He had his own live men to think of: AB and the Boy and Carpenter and Bo'sun and all the others, those he thought he knew almost as well as *Anna*.

Anna was straightforward. You could read her name backwards and you got the same result. The skipper talked with her about his pains, about the crew and his family at home, and old *Anna* pounded tirelessly towards England, lifting and dipping her bows in answer. He could not talk like that with any of the men, could not bewilder and frighten them with his own fears and despair. All that had to be shut up in his own worn-out mind, so that the others could keep their strength.

If their fear grew to breaking point in a critical situation, if fear showed in their eyes or voices or the hands that held the spokes of the wheel, he had to subdue his own fear, suppress it in his mind. But each time he did so, some of it remained and took root and grew with every fresh crossing he made. Each time it was a little more difficult to keep back, each time he had to summon up more strength of will in order to retain his self-control.

He had to force his voice to speak slowly and reassuringly, force out a little smile, the dangerous unpleasant smile that was supposed to provide evidence of strong nerves; the smile that irritated others and sometimes made them angry, but also steadied them. On many occasions he had noticed that that slight raising of the corners of his mouth could make the helmsman or look-out do their job better.

The Skipper ran his index finger across his cheek until it reached the place where a nerve was quivering and throbbing below the skin. He cursed this visible sign that not everything was as it should be with him, and the thought crossed his mind that if he took a couple of drams before he went to the office in Liverpool it might stop the twitch – otherwise some kindly person might start talking about doctors and taking leave. But in no circumstances could he go ashore and remain there for more than a few hours.

There had been a time when he had been afraid of losing *Anna* if he went on leave, but he could no longer pretend to himself that this was the main reason for his remaining aboard. Lying there in his bunk, *Anna's* Skipper knew that if he were to stay ashore for a few weeks, perhaps even a few days he would never get himself up the gangway again. The suppressed fears of several years of convoy work had permeated every cell in his body and he could only manage to go on sailing if he clung to the ship, did not leave her for longer than to rush to the Nortraship office, the workshops or a convoy conference. And if in the end he did not dare to go ashore at all, he could always make some excuse and send the First Mate in his place. His job was to sail and he must go on doing so until he dropped . . .

The Skipper again tried to close his aching, swollen eyes, but then the faces of his wife and two small sons came. It was more than two years since he had had news of them and this uncertainty about his three in Norway was more dreadful than the U-boats and the constant burden of responsibility for ship and men. Quite early on he had realized that if he was to lose his reason, the main cause would be this uncertainty about their fate and his longing for them. Night after night the thought of his wife and sons made sleep impossible, and in his despair he could raise his fists and strike out at the visions in his cabin.

Worst, perhaps, were the nights in port, the rare quiet nights when German bombers stayed away from where *Anna* was berthed and there was nothing to drive away thoughts of his family, nights when it would almost have been a relief if the air-raid sirens had begun to wail.

There had been times when he and the others aboard had left the ship and gone to a shelter in the docks. There in the cellar with its sour musty air, squeezed in with sucking babies, women knitting, beery dockers, and girls in uniform, in shabby everyday, wartime England, he felt best of all. In the flickering candlelight he would try to avoid the places where the men from the boat had clustered and forge through to a corner where he would be squeezed up with just a lot of strangers. There he might suddenly begin to talk. Not uncontrollably, not complainingly, but nonetheless about his own worries. Squeezed beside a mature woman, or better still an old one, he could talk about his sons. With men that he liked the look of he could talk about the ship and convoy work.

The Bo'sun was swearing at the Boy because he had dropped an empty matchbox on the deck – the words poured out in a variety of languages. But when, puce in the face, the Bo'sun had to stop to draw breath, his anger suddenly went. He fished in his pocket for his cigarettes, fumbled as he pulled one out of the packet and thrust it into the Boy's hand. They smoked in silence, but after a few pulls Bo'sun suddenly chuckled: 'One gets a bit crotchety at the end of a crossing, eh?' and he gave another deep-voiced chuckle.

The Boy gave a little laugh. 'You've got a rough side to your tongue, I must say.'

The wind tugged at the Boy's hair as he leaned out over

the rail and spat, just as the Bo'sun had done. On a sudden impulse Bo'sun slapped the Boy's shoulder and the Boy responded by thumping Bo'sun's chest.

'Oh, ho!' Bo'sun whinnied. 'You can use your fists all right, even if you're just the Boy.'

'I'll give you a proper thrashing ashore if you don't look out,' the Boy replied.

Bo'sun laughed good-humouredly and the Boy laughed with him. They were bubbling over with sudden mirth: they slapped each other on the shoulders and arms and roared with laughter, ending hanging gasping over the rail, their whole bodies feeling better for a good laugh.

Bo'sun had something to see to for'ard, but the Boy stayed where he was on the after deck wondering at the new, remarkable sensation of being alive. He took a deep breath, aware of the coolness of the rail against the palm of his hands, the worn deck beneath his feet, the wind against his cheek, and of Bo'sun as his comrade, a mountain of friendliness, a fortress of protective benevolence.

He pressed his stomach against the rail, drank in the air with mouth wide open and held his breath to expand his chest, drawing his shoulders back as he did so. He felt so alive that he had the sensation of being immortal, of being able to take a walk on the sea, trotting round *Anna*, taking a great leap across the water and then little jumps from wave to wave. He gave a chuckle at the idea and spat into the sea, as Bo'sun had, in ecstatic arrogance.

He felt dreadfully hungry and ran to the galley to ask if he could have a bit extra, a lot extra, a great plateful of more for the Bo'sun's best friend and one who spat at death in the sea.

But in the galley they were furious at him for badgering between meals and that soon made him angry too. It was a common thing, this sudden switch from one moment's aggression to profuse amiability and gaiety. They were still in the danger zone and *Anna* might be sunk before she had another cable's length behind her. They who had sailed so long already, had survived so many thousand miles at sea and were soon to see the coast, might never reach it.

Fear and hope collided in their minds; for the last few hours at sea it was like having the stern in hell and the bows in heaven, and they would feel like this until the mooring ropes had been made fast on the quay and they could hear the wonderful stillness that came when the engines stopped.

Now at last they had the Irish Sea behind them and were going up the Mersey to the docks in Liverpool. *Anna* was one of the ten to reach port – ten out of the thirty-six that had sailed in convoy from the coast of America.

PART TWO

Donkeyman had watch below and was shaving, so hurriedly that he kept nicking his skin, but he was so wild for beer and whisky and land underfoot that he had no time to be careful. He could always wash the thin trickles of blood off in the lavatory when he got to the bar. He could wait to tie his laces until he had downed a beer or two, even wait to put on his tie that he stuffed in his pocket, until, say, his third whisky.

He almost ran off the ship and to the bar that was only a couple of hundred yards up Dock Road. He would soon be back aboard again, singing and bellowing for more of his wages to be paid him.

The Second Mate, he who had sat in the swung-out lifeboat, and Greaser, who had refused to 'behave decently', had also gone ashore – only they had gone for always and said goodbye to no one.

The Boy walked down the gangway with a number of the others. They were excited and delighted by the feel of firm ground under their feet and hurried away, hungry for life and thirsting for drink. Passing a store the Boy stopped, though none of the others would wait. Against the wall stood an ancient black bicycle. The Boy looked round at the others. They were already well up near the dock gates. It was taking them all their time to keep up with Bo'sun striding towards his bar.

The Boy walked hesitantly towards the bicycle and took tentative hold of the handlebars, looking round as he did so. There was no one in sight. He flung his leg over the saddle and rode round a bit on the quay.

He was only seventeen. He had seen many men die at sea and he rather wanted to see if he could still ride a bicycle because he often felt so old. He began riding round in figures of eight, making each figure smaller and the turns tighter until he had to turn the handlebars round so far that the bicycle toppled over.

There he lay on his face with the hard paving stones of the old quay under him. He lay quite still as if dead, feeling happy that it was so hard and unyielding under him: no up and down motion, no torpedoes beneath that surface. He lay there wishing he was somewhere where there was earth to walk on, proper earth, miles and miles of it, earth to take hold of, to stand on, lie on, to smell and to taste. Earth to stamp and trample, to run on and see all round you in every direction as far as your eye could see.

The front wheel of the bicycle had stopped spinning. Bo'sun and the others were on their second glass, when the Boy felt the pressure of a shoe against his back. He turned his head to the side; the shoe moved away, but at the same time a great fist took hold of the scruff of his neck. A man in labourer's clothes pulled him to his feet and began cursing and pointing to the bicycle and brandishing his fist under the Boy's nose. The Boy did not understand much of what the docker said, but the word 'police' was clear enough. The Boy was afraid and kept stuttering:

'I sailor – Norwegian sailor.'

The docker had a firm grip of his upper arm and dragged him back in the direction of the quay.

The Carpenter was a bit behind the others in going ashore. When he was a few paces from the ship, he saw a strange man dragging the Boy along behind him. He called out and ran towards them. Reaching them, he took a good grip of the Boy with one hand and caught hold of the docker with the other. There were not many people could twist out of the Carpenter's grip.

The Boy explained about the bicycle, then the Carpenter got going in English. He did not say much: merely that the Boy was seventeen and had just crossed the Atlantic in a convoy, in which most of the ships had been lost. The docker shook his head; a kindly expression came over his face and he patted the Boy's shoulder.

'All right – everything's all right.'

The Carpenter took the docker off to the bar with him.

The Skipper left *Anna* a good hour after the Carpenter. On the quay he paused and studied his ship from stem to stern. Even he had to admit that she could have had better lines. Her funnel was straight and tall and old-fashioned; the bridge and midships clumsy and oversized. His gaze followed the masts and booms and stopped at the aged gun and the new flag on the stern. That flag was their country afloat – the only visible sign that they had a country, that they came from anywhere and were not just beings without identity who belonged body and soul to the sea.

In many convoys he had seen a Norwegian flag in every column and it had become almost a habit to count the number of Norwegian ships as soon as daylight came. He was accustomed to this number being smaller every dawn, but had never been able to regard these losses as inevitable 'expenditure in the accounts of war'. Every boat gone made him grieve for the fate of those in her, and each loss fed his hatred of the Germans and their U-boats.

Angrily he flung down a newly lighted cigarette and ground it to pieces with his heel. Then he lit a fresh cigarette: he must make himself appear calm and friendly when he went to the bar to meet the men.

He walked quietly to the dock gates and hurried up Dock Road. He wanted to get to the bar before any of the men went off with a woman or moved on to another place where fresh, full glasses would appear on the table to greet them.

The Skipper did not have to search for his men. They always went first in a group to the Bo'sun's Liverpool bar. Spirits were high when he entered. The men knew that he would come and were looking forward to the moment when he would forge his way to the bar, take off his cap with its faded braid and say: 'This is my round.'

The glasses would all be filled and the men would drink the Skipper's health, while he drained his glass in reply knowing that they liked to see him down a glass without drawing breath. Somehow that made them feel better about getting tight, as they would that night and the next and the next, as long as their money lasted and *Anna* was still in port.

The Boy was seated beside Bo'sun. When Bo'sun drank, the Boy drank. When Bo'sun smoked, the Boy smoked. Drink had made him strong and martial. He could not stop talking about the hit they had scored on the U-boat, and in the commotion said to the Skipper:

'The fellows think we could disable a cruiser, if we could just hit its magazine with the first shot . . .'

The Skipper felt a surge of anger mounting in him, but when he saw the Boy's expectant face his indignation vanished as swiftly as it had come. In a few days' time the Boy might be drifting about in the sea, dead, and even if he imagined that *Anna*'s old gun could sink the entire German fleet, that was no reason to shatter his childish fantasies.

'Skal, Boy,' the Skipper said, and smiling, added: 'AB's the chap to do it, too. He's been in the Navy.'

The Boy was delighted. He tried to think of others in *Anna* who were 'damned fine chaps', and wanted the Skipper to sit at their table as long as possible. He had never thought the Skipper could be 'such a pal'.

'Carpenter got our flag up again quick enough, didn't he? Showed those damned Germans that even if they ran us down, they can't down our flag!'

The Skipper nodded, but now his expression had become serious, and the Carpenter set his glass down on the table so hard that it cracked. 'If they knock the flag-pole down,' he said, 'I'll lash it to an oar again and if they shoot *Anna* to little pieces, may the devil tattoo me. I'll hold the flag up with one arm and swim with the other.'

At that they all wanted to drink with the Carpenter. Donkeyman began to bawl a chorus, but Bo'sun wouldn't have any singing and Donkeyman shut up and sat and sulked, swaying in his chair. Drink had now made the others solemn and they made enormous efforts to make their talk factual and to pronounce every syllable, for the Skipper was still there and had just said, 'Five Norwegian flags went down in that last convoy.'

They spoke the ships' names but without sentimentality or any resemblance to a memorial service. It was a mere statement of fact that such and such ships were gone for ever, that so and so had been in them whom they had met in bars in Brooklyn, Newcastle, Hongkong or Port of Spain.

The Skipper always stayed an hour with them in the bar on the first day in port. Now he had done his hour. He got to his feet, walked out and back to the ship and solitude.

Now Donkeyman could bawl and sing without anyone hushing him. Then he fished out a stained family snapshot and his voice was thick as he told them about it, but no one listened. They only pretended to admire the picture. They had seen it a hundred times before. But Donkeyman became more and more moved by his monologue and more beer stains appeared on the photograph.

AB was standing in a corner with three girls. He waggled his hips and his hands described curves over his thighs and chest, then he went round peering gravely into the face of every woman in the bar, inspecting the colour of her eyes.

Bo'sun was narking at Sparks who had been boring him with new details of the radio shop he was going to start once the war was over. It was not that Sparks had avoided standing his round, what irritated Bo'sun was that Sparks should save a bit every month. Every time Sparks increased his imaginary turnover and opened a new branch, Bo'sun exclaimed irritatedly: 'What are you saving for? Do you think you'll live to enjoy it? Drink what you have and don't be a fool!'

Then Sparks gave Bo'sun the sort of condescending look he imagined a big businessman would direct at an ignorant sailor. Frowning above eyes that were watering from all the drink he had had, he said: 'Capital is necessary if you want a big, efficient business.' But Bo'sun was immune to mercantile truisms and just exclaimed even more loudly: 'What are you saving for? Do you think you'll live to enjoy it?'

The Carpenter was dancing with the woman they called Convoy Molly. She had a big frame and red hair and her great breasts were like fenders between her and Carpenter's impressive, demanding body.

The tune was a foxtrot and everyone on the crowded floor was dancing with quick, brisk steps – everyone, that is, except the Carpenter and Molly. The Carpenter was dancing a slow waltz. He never danced anything else, no matter what the band happened to play. For a while he might just stand in the middle of the crowd of dancing couples, like a lighthouse in a rough sea, then he would lead Molly off again on his own course and in his own rhythm. If he wanted to turn and there was not room, his arms would tighten round her waist and Molly, groaning and at the same time neighing with delight, would be lifted up while her partner blissfully pivoted in semicircles.

Then the Carpenter felt thirsty again. He bent down, put his arms under Molly's jutting hams and lifted her up till her mop of red hair touched the ceiling light and stood round her like a halo of gold and bronze. The lamp swung to and fro and as drunken men watched the swaying shade they were half at sea and half ashore. The Carpenter carried his partner to his chair and took her on his knees. The table was covered with glasses, full, half full. Round followed round. They sang and bellowed, squabbled and comforted, drank and danced, wept and laughed. They had to live quickly; live and feel everything all at once. There was no time to wait for things to happen tomorrow. It must be now.

The Carpenter noticed that the Boy was staring at Convoy Molly, staring out of swimming eyes at her swelling bosom; so he lifted Molly off his lap and shoved her down on a chair; then he picked up the Boy and placed him on Molly's lap. The Boy tried to get up, but Molly held on to him and he was so full of drink that he soon stopped struggling. It was pleasantly warm on Molly and the Boy fell asleep.

The Carpenter continued to get beer for Molly and himself, and Bo'sun thrust a pound note into Molly's hand so that she should stay where she was and let the Boy sleep.

From behind the bar came the call 'Time, gentlemen, please!' and Carpenter told Donkeyman to take his jersey off and knot the arms and neck. He wanted it as a sack to carry some bottles back aboard. They were still singing and shouting to each other when above the din of it all came the sudden penetrating wail of the sirens.

There was no panic. There had been so many raids already, so many bombs had fallen, in winter, spring and autumn. The sailors were the calmest of them all. They went to the shelter with the others. Not that that was anything new. They had done it before and it even gave them an absurd feeling of security to be ashore and able to run for cover, just to have somewhere to run to and firm ground under their feet instead of a swaying deck and nothing but air between them and the planes.

Strangely enough they felt less defenceless when death threatened from the skies above than when it lay waiting for them beneath the surface of the sea. And if they were hit by a bomb ashore, being maimed or killed along with a number of others in a shelter seemed less pointless there than out in the Atlantic.

The Boy was dazed with tiredness and alcohol and he lurched about blindly as they streamed towards the door; but Molly had a firm grip of his hand and she towed him like a dinghy behind her through the sea of people. In the shelter he went to sleep again in her arms.

For some twenty days he had been tensed ready to dash for lifeboat or raft, and for more than twenty times twenty days his hunger for tenderness had never found more than a pat on the shoulder from Bo'sun or the Carpenter or a kindly 'How are you, Boy?' from the Chief. The woman sitting there on a box in the shelter was large and warm. When she felt that her tenderness towards the slight figure had turned his sexual hunger into a child's insatiable need of protective goodness, she cradled him on her quivering thighs and stroked his mop of hair, plastered with lotion though it was. The Boy sank deeper and deeper into restful sleep, down through layers of fear deposited by each successive journey until he was back to where he had been before his first bombing, and then deeper still.

Bombs fell, some near, some in the distance. Houses burst into flames, factories collapsed, streets were reduced to rubble and in the port ships capsized. Wreaths on a fresh grave were sent hurtling through the darkness, and wooden crosses rained down into the old churchyard like crashing planes. Three firemen were squirting water on a burning building. The next moment water was pouring from a severed hose into a still-smoking crater. There was no longer anyone to put out the fire. When a third bomb hit the self-same spot, the mains pipe was shattered and a high column of water shot up into the night and splashed down on rubble, twisted iron, half a mattress, some broken beams with a few fluttering strips of ceiling paper, and a severed leg.

More bombs fell, as if dropped by blind men. Down in the

shelter Molly realized that the city was being badly mishandled that night. Yet what was happening outside the walls of concrete and sandbags was of less concern to her at that moment than the Boy she still rocked with a profound sense of tenderness in the heart beneath her red jumper.

Eventually the explosions stopped and the sirens announced the All Clear. She woke the Boy and got him on to his feet. She swore softly, for she was aching all over from having sat in the same position so long with the Boy on her lap. She wanted to get back to see if the house where she rented a room was still standing.

They went out into the dark and set off down the street. The air was sharp and acrid with smoke from fires and the smell of explosives. Snarling Spitfires were still in the air above the city: from the districts where there were fires came the sound of the clanging bells of fire-engines and ships' sirens were wailing out in the port.

For a moment the Boy wondered whether *Anna* had been hit or not. But he was not letting go of Convoy Molly's hand and when she found the building intact, she led him up the narrow stairs.

She did not switch on the light, but instead pulled back the curtains and stood by the window looking at the orange flames in the night sky above many parts of the town.

It was years since the Boy had been in a home and in Molly's room he felt more secure than anywhere he had been. The darkness in there was warm and soft, the walls would protect him from harm. The Boy trembled with joyful well-being, as he snuffed in the room's various smells: cigarettes, scent, woman, dust, drink and food. He saw Molly's plump shape and her mop of hair softly outlined against the night outside the window, and the quiet was so good that he raised his arms in the direction where she stood and then slowly closed his hands as though filling them with the security of her room.

She yawned a long, audible yawn, then stretched. She came towards the chair in which he sat, took hold of his feet and removed his shoes; then she leaned forward and undid his tie and unbuttoned his shirt, and he sat quite still inhaling the smell of her.

Then she undressed and as he still sat there in the chair, she took a good-humoured grip of his forelock and led him to the bed. He moved over to the wall and made himself as small as he could. The bed creaked and Convoy Molly lay down beside him. The mattress was as soft and thick as she, and the bed became the trough between two gentle waves and the Boy drifted into her comforting white arms. And when he fell asleep, although he was at sea there was no ammunition ships exploding there; instead, he dreamed his best dream which had been reality one summer morning ten years before. He dreamed of lying right out in the bows of the old, white fishing smack, half asleep and half awake. He could hear the water rippling against the thin plank on which his ear rested and when he looked aft past the mast there was his elder brother on the central thwart and his father at the tiller . . .

When the sirens started wailing, *Anna*'s Skipper was lying in his cabin trying to get to sleep.

There were many German planes making for Liverpool. The drone of their engines was like a continuous roar high up in the night sky. Before he had time to get up on deck, he heard the whistle and rattle of bombs, explosions and the crack of the AA guns. There were air-raid shelters in the docks, of course, but the Skipper thought he might as well stay aboard and he went up on to the bridge to get a better view of what was happening.

The Chief also came up on to the bridge and stood in the

wing nearest land. He looked in over the flaming, exploding city, and in his slow voice, said, 'It's a queer thing with the land, but there is a comfort in knowing that perhaps you will be found, if things go wrong.'

The bombers were over the port, too, and one ship was hit not far away. Mud and stones spattered round them and they were momentarily deafened by the explosion.

A flare burst and the Skipper saw the Chief's lips moving, but his eardrums were still out of action so that, when he tried to tell him he did not catch what he said, he could not even hear his own voice. He shook his head and pointed to his ears, and the Chief nodded.

As the Skipper thought how much a matter of chance it was whether one lived or died, all at once he became quite indifferent to his own fate. He was so tired that Death was no longer frightening, but the only possible way of being allowed to rest. In any case convoy work would kill him in one way or another. Even if *Anna* remained afloat until the war was over, convoy work would have turned him into a man who just could not live as other people did.

The light of the flare had shown him how old and exhausted the Chief looked, had let him read in the man's face and short-sighted eyes what the convoys had done to him, how every crossing had left its mark on him like the rings in a tree trunk. And the Skipper realized that he did not have the Chief's strength; no one in *Anna* was stronger than the mild, round-shouldered Chief.

These were not thoughts the Skipper liked. Early on, he had formed his own picture of what a skipper should think and do and had worked himself into his part inspired by the responsibility, traditions of the sea and the authority of command.

Command? No one had asked him if he wanted to sail from USA to Liverpool with a cargo of mines, bombs, shells and nitro-glycerine. He just had to go up on to his bridge and stay there day after day, while the convoy made its way at snail's pace across the Atlantic. And the crew had to do as he said, without him asking them whether they wanted to do it or not.

Ashore were men who decided what he and his crew and his ship had to do. And these men too would die when their time came, but of some illness and weakness of old age and in a bed surrounded by their family and clergymen. And while they were alive, they made money from ships that sailed the seas, while the deck-hands and bo'suns and donkeymen and others had £20–£25 a month and orders to sail to hell and back, and none got so much as a mention in the newspapers if he was blown to little pieces or turned into a flaming torch on a burning tanker. Their families could not even lay a wreath on their graves, because no one could tell them where the remains of husband, son or father were . . .

Even if a million wreaths were laid on the waters of the Atlantic from many coasts, and millions of others were blown by the winds and carried by the currents, the ocean was so huge that only those with blind faith could ever comfort themselves with the thought that a single wreath would drift across the graveless remains in the deep. Nor would they ever receive any military honour. Who had ever seen a monument to 'The Unknown Sailor'?

The authorities did not even recognize the men of the Merchant Navy as servicemen. The Carpenter and AB and others of *Anna*'s crew had fired off the gun at the U-boat and on several occasions in *Anna* they had stood clutching machine-guns in a hopeless attempt to fight off German planes; yet they were still classed as civilians. It meant nothing to the authorities that the country had far more casualties among the Merchant Navy than in the Army or Air Force, or that the Allied leaders said that the men of the Norwegian Merchant Fleet were worth more to the war effort than a million soldiers.

The men in the convoys wore dungarees, not khaki. They were not entitled to the same compensation and pension as even a lieutenant working in an office in London who fell under a bus. Their job was to sail and die, as nameless as draught animals in a jungle full of beasts of prey.

His eardrums still hurt, but they had recovered enough for him to realize that the Chief had spoken his name. The Skipper looked in the direction in which the Chief was pointing. By the light of a burning building he saw four or five men running about the roof of another large building shovelling up incendiary bombs and throwing them down into the street. Then another bomb fell on the far side of the dock and the Chief said:

'That was pretty close too.'

'You should have gone to a shelter long ago,' the Skipper said.

'You too,' the Chief replied.

They looked up again at the building and the men running about its roof several storeys above ground trying to save it, and again a strange thought came to the Skipper. He thought that the man who owned that big building was most unlikely to be one of those running about the roof with shovels dealing with incendiaries. Men who owned large buildings were administrators and if their property went up in flames they got insurance money and would be able to build an even bigger one after the war. For that sort of man usually survived a war, while those who were running about that roof probably owned nothing. And up there they were quite unprotected, having nothing but the smoky air between them and the roaring enemy planes.

The Skipper turned and looked out towards the sea. He found himself longing to be in a convoy again, out at sea where every second he had to concentrate on the ship's course, her place in the column, and torpedoes, where he had to be the skipper all the time and his mind never got filled with bewildering thoughts about other people's parts in the great war. He found himself longing for the splash of the bow wave and the even hum of the engines, for the open sea and the struggle with the elements which demanded all that he had been trained to do and lived for: to get his ship and cargo skilfully and safely from port to port . . .

On the fourth day in Liverpool the Carpenter turned out at the usual time, sounded the bilges and tanks, informed No. 1 and noted the result on the blackboard at the entrance to the engine-room. When he entered the mess again for more coffee, Donkeyman had also put in an appearance; Donkeyman had already consumed a couple of bottles of beer and was 'happy' once more. He still had a few shillings left from the previous night's binge and the certainty that further quantities of beer and whisky awaited him only a few minutes from the ship made him feel utterly carefree. The Chief had said that he could go ashore again that day, and *Anna* was the best boat in the world and the Carpenter and the Chief the finest chaps in the world, and even the grey daylight above the port was the loveliest light he had ever seen. Before he had even tasted the coffee he called to the Cook that it was first class. The Carpenter just *had* to go with him to the bar. They all must, and he would stand them a glass or two. Donkeyman had enough left for at least fifteen glasses and what happened after the fifteen was of no interest at that moment.

But the Carpenter had an errand in the city that morning. He had received a message that he was to go to the Consulate and fetch a medal; you got one after eighteen months in the Allied Merchant Fleet. The Carpenter had not been looking for rewards and did not bother about medals or distinctions. He had seen quite enough to know that medals are not always pinned on the chests of those who have earned them. He would much rather have had fifty quid in cash than a bit of copper to put at the bottom of his chest. It must have been the Skipper who had put their names forward, his and AB's, Sparks's and the Chief's. They had all been in *Anna* since the German invasion of Norway.

The Skipper had given the message to each individually but they went ashore together and set off for the Consulate in a body. AB, tall and thin, head drooping; the Chief, round-shouldered and peering, wearing his old serge suit, Sparks in a well-pressed uniform, and the huge figure of the Carpenter in a dark-coloured jacket, fists thrust so deep into his trousers-pockets that the waistband was pulled down on to his hips.

They were embarrassed and felt shy with each other. They wanted the medal and yet they didn't. A medal was a visible sign that you had done something and that was a nice thing. Almost always the cargo they had brought across the ocean was unloaded and taken away without them having any visible, direct proof that what they had risked their lives to get was actually being used in the struggle with the enemy. Some seamen did ocasionally stop to think that the bombs and shells and all the other things they had ferried across the Atlantic were going to be dropped or fired by men in battle-dress on other men in green uniforms with '*Gott mit Uns*' on their belt buckles, on German territory and on ships flying the swastika flag. They might even envisage just their bombs and ammunition being used against Germans in Norway, but that was all just make-believe. Their one actual contact was when they had sailed *Anna* to a French port with a cargo of tanks in the spring of 1940, and they had lived on the memory of that ever since.

The quay had looked like a battlefield. The tanks had scarcely got their tracks on to firm ground before the British had jumped in, started up and disappeared in a cloud of dust in the direction of the enemy. The front was so close that *Anna*'s crew must have heard the guns of the tanks being fired, only it was impossible to distinguish individual bangs or explosions in what was a continuous roar.

Since then they had been in the monotonous horror of convoy work, and in memory they had embroidered and embellished pretty well everything that had taken place before they began crossing the Atlantic in the treadmill of terror that convoys were. Because of this their mental picture of the day they brought the British those tanks was now about as realistic as a funeral without a corpse.

Progress towards the Consulate was far from swift. The Chief got out of breath very easily, and, being unaccustomed to visiting offices, the Carpenter found he required a few drinks to give him courage, so they went into a bar. Sparks insisted on paying and because he was one who actually saved, the Carpenter and AB drank up quicker than they had intended when they first went in. The Chief drank lemonade as he always did on the few occasions he set a foot inside such a place.

'We'll have to go, seeing the Skipper's got it for us,' the Carpenter said.

'He's a good man,' the Chief added.

'Has he had a medal himself?' AB wondered. The beer was beginning to have an effect.

'He's never mentioned it,' the Chief said.

'He never says anything,' the Carpenter said. 'I've been sailing with him between Lime Street and Court Street for the last two years and scarcely heard him open his mouth.'

They fell silent again, busied themselves with their glasses and cigarettes while the Chief polished his glasses that were clean and bright, and when he had finished with them he scraped at a speck of grease on the table-top. So many people had been through even worse and not been given a medal. They had another drink and felt even worse about their medals.

'Bugger . . .' AB muttered, letting his head hang. Then he remembered that the Chief was there and begged his pardon;

but the Chief had not heard him swear. He had been thinking about all those who had been killed and drowned at sea, in the Arctic, Atlantic, Pacific, Mediterranean and elsewhere – those who were gone for ever without getting a medal.

There were some British ratings in the bar. They had shoved several tables together and were sitting round them, drinking and singing. When they struck up 'Auld Lang Syne' the Carpenter said it meant they were due to sail in a few hours' time.

He had heard that song many times before, though never like that time in Le Havre in 1940, when *Anna* made her second trip to the Continent. She had a cargo of war materials and arrived in the middle of the fighting. Tanks and armoured cars were rattling up and down the streets, planes dive-bombing the town and guns blazing away.

The English were in a trap and had to be rescued. A large troopship lay ready to put out across the Channel. She was full, with soldiers crowded like sardines on the deck. Then two German bombers came over. Their bombs hit the troopship, which heeled over. Then her side was covered with crawling men like ants and hundreds dived into the sea. A British trawler was manœuvred in, a wonderful feat of seamanship, and she picked up, or rather scooped men out of the water and put in to the quay with her decks packed tight from stem to stern.

The men were all soaked and exhausted, many of them wounded, yet as the trawler passed *Anna*, the Carpenter had heard singing: they were singing 'Auld Lang Syne'. And the Carpenter remembered how when *Anna* got back to England from that trip to the war-torn coast of France they had gone into a bar and met some lads from the Navy like those sitting in that bar. The British had asked who they were and where they had come from; and when they heard that they were Norwegians who had got out of Le Havre with their ship they stood them round after round. Then they had felt strangely allied, not just because they were fighting for the same cause, but as people.

The Chief drank his lemonade and the Carpenter drained his glass. Then he fished out his last pound note and ordered a round for the Navy men.

'Why should you pay for men in uniform?' AB asked irritably.

'As a return for that song,' the Carpenter replied.

'If you're so fond of the Navy you should join up,' Sparks jeered.

'Do you think I would wear uniform, you stripey creep,' the Carpenter shouted, glaring furiously at the wireless operator's officer's jacket.

He felt rather silly having sat there almost sober, and got up and spent a quid on standing British sailors a round. He squinted at Sparks and hissed:

'You, Piggy-bank, what do you think you're saving for? Do you think you're going to live for ever?'

'We'd best get on up to the Consulate,' the Chief put in.

The British sailors waved to them as they went out, but the Carpenter was sulking and angry and walked straight to the door without looking to right or left. He was going at such a speed that he collided with a youth with a bulging kit-bag on his shoulder. The youth reminded him of himself when, at the age of fourteen, he had got his first berth in a deep-water ship. In the twenties there just had not been any decent jobs going where he lived. He had seen other boys coming home with kitbags, blue jackets, black caps with shiny peaks, American cigarettes, and money, and there had been an aura of tar, salt spray, adventure and palm trees about them.

The encounter drove Le Havre and the money he had spent on the British sailors from his mind. Now he was thinking of his family in Norway and was glad about the medal. It would be a nice thing to have in his drawer or even framed and hung up on the wall – if he survived. It wouldn't be bad if neighbours and others who came in could see that he had not been away all those years doing nothing.

AB had not been in the Liverpool Consulate since April 1940. *Anna* had been making for Norway with a cargo of grain, but like all Norwegian ships she had obeyed the order to make at once for an Allied or neutral port, so she had turned round in the North Sea and gone to Liverpool. They had been like a band of brothers during those two days it took them to get to Alexandra Dock. Old antipathies were swept away. The deck-hands had never once mentioned 'sweat-rag', while those in the engine-room seemed to have forgotten that there were such words as 'swab'.

Many of them, of course, had wanted to go straight back to Norway and fight and they had put on their best trousers and sweaters and gone to the Consulate in a body as now, crowding along the pavement.

One chap they called Hongkong Olsen was the most vehement. He had not set foot in Norway for fifteen years. It was all the same to him where he was as long as he could be in a bar drinking, but in April 1940 he could not wait to get back.

Hongkong Olsen had given one thump on the Consul's door and marched straight in with seven or eight of the others at his heels. The Consul had not been able to get them home and had explained that there would not even be enough rifles for all who wanted to go to Norway and fight.

'We'll take pitch-forks and axes,' Hongkong Olsen had called out. But it was no use, and when they got back aboard *Anna* the Skipper had said the same as the Consul: that the Allies had more use for good seamen than for soldiers. So they had stayed in her – all, that is, except Hongkong Olsen. He had signed off and joined the British Navy.

On this occasion the Chief knocked rather timidly and stood waiting for a while until a woman opened the door.

The sailors thought she smelled like blue anemones at home.

Sparks was the weakest from the drink and at the Consulate he tried to make a little speech. The Chief just said: 'My very sincere thanks,' AB mumbled 'Thanks,' and the Carpenter could not get anything out at all.

The Chief wanted to get straight back to the ship, but the other three went to a bar for a few more drinks. They had orders to be aboard again by midnight and they all knew only too well what that meant.

AB had enough money for one round and Sparks for several. The Carpenter wanted to dance, he had to have one more slow waltz before he sailed in another convoy. The bar-girl tried a few tango steps, because the pianist was playing a tango, but the Carpenter was not open to compromise. Some of the others began to smile at him, but then the pianist, seeing the great size of him, switched to a slow waltz.

As he stumped round in his last waltz the Carpenter was tight, broke and content, and when he got back to the table he said to AB: 'That brown-eyed girl of yours will like the medal . . .'

When the three had spent their last shilling, the girls in the bar stood them drinks on their own account. Sparks swaggered and said they were smart girls who could see who was a sailor and who not.

'Nonsense,' Carpenter said. 'They worship Churchill and remember what he said about seamen in that speech he made in the warehouse in Alexandra Dock . . .'

Eight others from *Anna* came into the bar. They still had money and more rounds were drunk. When the time came to go aboard, they knocked back one last dram and chaser. It might be a long time before they had another – if ever.

Bo'sun still had some money. He fished in all his pockets and laid a crumpled note and a number of coins on the dirty table-top. The others who had anything left did the same, and it made quite a little heap. When they could not find another penny, Bo'sun picked up the whole table and took it across to where an old woman had been sitting for a long time over one glass of beer.

'Here,' Bo'sun said, putting the table down in front of her. She stared at him, surprised and eager at the same time, guessing the money was for her, yet not daring to take it. 'Here you are,' Bo'sun repeated. 'Money for you from Norwegian sailors.'

A thin hand was laid over the little pile of notes and coins before she looked up and thanked him.

Then they gave each of the bar-girls a hug and walked out noisily and down to the quay and their ship.

PART THREE

Anna left Liverpool as day broke. Several other ships sailed at the same time along with an escort vessel for the big convoy assembling off the coast.

The convoy conference at the Naval office had been no different from the many others the Skipper had attended. They had been given the usual instructions what to do *if* U-boats should attack – as if they did not always attack a convoy; the usual orders about keeping 'close up' in column no matter what happened; and then the sealed envelope, which must never be opened until the ship was out at sea. That envelope contained all the details of the assembly area for the convoy, the route to be sailed and any special measures to be taken during the crossing.

The Skipper was always very particular about his envelope. He took it from the conference in an old black briefcase. He was determined no one was going to snatch this from him and so he had had a narrow strap fastened to the handle and buckled the other end round his lower arm. Things would be even easier for the U-boats if German spies in England were able to get hold of convoy envelopes with all the information about assembly areas, sailing times and routes. Back on board, he put the envelope in a special box he kept in the chart-house. This was made of lead and perforated, so that it would sink instantly if thrown into the sea, as it would have to be if the enemy attempted to board the ship or if she was sinking and had to be abandoned after an attack.

It had proved relatively easy to get a new second mate and a new greaser in Liverpool. The rest of the crew were the same. It rather surprised the Skipper that more of his men had not asked to be signed off in England. He was particularly worried about the Cook, AB and the Boy. The Cook appeared to have made a swift recovery, but there was no doubt that he needed a longish period of care and rest ashore. The Boy and AB had stood the last trip back to England well but lately something had come over them both. The Boy had begun to drink, he was thinner and often gloomy and in the last few days in Liverpool he had shirked. AB had periods of being strangely remote. When at the wheel during the last trip he had on several occasions failed to hear orders to alter course, and stood there as if deaf, not reacting until the officer of the watch had gone and given him a shake.

They were all obviously worn out both mentally and physically, but they had to keep on sailing. The Allies would be lost if they did not get food, petrol, oil and munitions; so the men in *Anna* and thousands of other cargo ships of many nationalities had to go to sea again and again and again, and to sail as long as they could stagger about a deck. If someone felt he could face no more of it and tried to hide himself ashore, the police would hunt him out in bar, hotel, park, wood, street-corner or railway carriage and hound him back aboard another ship to sail in other convoys.

It was a grey day and the wind biting. Every now and then an extra strong gust whistled in the rigging and ventilators. The Skipper was grateful they were no longer encumbered with the barrage balloons that in the early days had floated above them until they were well away from the coast. The balloon might well make a German pilot think twice before he came too low over a ship, but with a wind as strong as the one then blowing the long wire holding it would have made a hellish monotonous noise. He remembered standing on the bridge in a pitch-black night listening to the wind on the wire: it was like music from icy, empty space, and he had wondered whether that was the music people heard on their way to the Kingdom of the Dead.

The Boy was at the wheel. He had been reprimanded by the Skipper because of his shirking in Liverpool and stood there very intent on keeping *Anna* exactly on course. The Skipper lit a cigarette; then suddenly he turned and offered one to the Boy. The Boy's face flushed with pleasure, as he stammered his thanks. The Skipper went out on to the wing. He regretted the impulsive offer. To offer the helmsman a cigarette was a breach of discipline but he had done it because the Boy had enough to fear as it was. He turned in towards the wheelhouse and was pleased to see that the Boy had not taken advantage of the situation to have a smoke while at the wheel, but had put the cigarette in his pocket.

Four hours later *Anna* reached the assembly area for the convoy. The Commodore's ship was ahead of the others and the boats that were to be in the first line stationed themselves to port and starboard of the leading ship and in line with her. Then came the next line and took up position exactly behind those in the first line and so it went on until all the ships were in their correct stations in the columns. There was supposed to be eighty metres between each ship and those ahead and astern of it, and slightly less to those on its beam.

When the armada of merchant ships was assembled in perfect order, the Commodore increased speed to the regulation seven knots of the slow convoy. A few of the boats may have been carrying whisky for America, but most were in ballast. Thus, except for those in tankers, the crews had a good chance of not being killed by the torpedoes. Tankers were explosive even in ballast. All too often they were ordered out and joined a fresh convoy before the men had time to clean their tanks properly. Residue at the bottom of tanks could form gas and that was, if possible, even more dangerous than having a full cargo of petrol.

With every mile, as the coast receded behind them, their voices became lower and lower and conversation tended to slacken. The sea ahead of them seemed so endless. They were going to be out of sight of land day after day, and they knew there was no protection or cleverness that could ensure a safe crossing. They could only hope that the torpedoes would not hit them and that on this occasion it would be them who would go down; for some ships were always lost.

On this occasion *Anna* was stationed well inside the convoy, and that made the men feel far better than when she had been on the outside with nothing between her and the attacking U-boats. *Anna* was number thirty-six, sixth from the leading ship of the third column.

The ships in the first line on either side of the Commodore's ship had numbers that ended with a figure one: first number eleven, then twenty-one, then thirty-one, then forty-one and so on to ninety-one. In the next line it was numbers twelve twenty-two, thirty-two and so on to ninety-two. The entire convoy consisted of eighty-one ships in nine columns, their crews totalling between two thousand and three thousand men.

As usual there were many Norwegian boats in this convoy. The Skipper stood with his glasses to his eyes looking at their flags. He had a long look at a big Norwegian tanker to starboard, number forty-two. The tanker's captain and he had been shipmates in younger days, and they had attended the same school when taking their mate's certificate and had spent much of their spare time together.

The Skipper had few friends. He was a solitary man in a ship and before the war his leaves in Norway had been very brief. Between each leave he had been months, sometimes even years at sea without ever getting to a Norwegian port, and so at home he had to make efforts to establish the contact he considered necessary between sons and their father. His boys were shy and hesitant at first, and, being very small, they had called him 'that man' for the first few days. By the time they had really become *his* sons, he had had to go back to sea again.

He had not made any lasting friendships since he had been a junior and still acquiring his certificates. On the rare occasions when he had to go to a party, he was by no means negative or unforthcoming, but it was unusual for him to be able to achieve real contact with anyone. He was perfectly happy sitting listening, and he did not forget what he thought worth remembering. But the captain of the tanker was one of his few friends and the fact that they were in the same convoy made it somehow easier to contemplate the endless expanse of water that lay ahead of *Anna*.

A sudden briskness came into the Skipper's movements and there was an eagerness in his eyes as his gazc brushed the mate before he ran down the ladder and went into his saloon. He went to his desk, opened the top drawer and produced a well-worn notebook. Yes, he had remembered correctly. It was his friend the tanker captain's birthday in two days' time. He almost ran up the ladder back to the bridge. He wanted to send a signal at once, for as soon as darkness fell you were allowed only to transmit vital visual signals to the Commodore, or receive them from him. There was absolute radio silence, for the Germans intercepted everything in the air. That was why they were not allowed to listen in on ordinary wirelesses in their messes or cabins, because uncontrolled apparatus could act as a transmitter of signals. Only approved equipment in the radio stations was allowed to receive, so that they could get reports and messages from Allied stations. But it was still daylight so the Skipper was able to signal across: 'Many happy returns for the nineteenth.'

From the tanker came the answer: 'Thanks, old chap. We'll celebrate it together in port.'

The Skipper smiled. AB who was at the wheel and could not remember when he last saw the Skipper smile, felt as if a weight had been taken off his mind. He would have liked to smile to the Skipper himself, but he did not quite dare, though the corners of his mouth twitched. Then the Skipper looked in his direction and gave him a friendly nod, and AB raised his head and smiled back and there was such a light in those blue eyes that the Skipper felt an urge to tell the man at the wheel about his friend in the tanker. He tugged at the peak of his cap, moved the cap from side to side on his head to settle it, gave a little cough, took a short step towards the wheel. But then he turned right round and was standing in his usual position with his back to the wheel and his eyes ceaselessly scanning the waters and the ships. For a long time his eyes were on the tanker, while he thought of his friend, who was now about forty-seven. They were roughly of an age. He himself had been forty-seven that spring. If the U-boats did not get one, or both of them, they would sail side by side all the way to America. It was the thought of the U-boats that had made him hurry with his message though the tanker captain's birthday was not for another two days. And the answer had come as naturally as if it was usual to be wished many happy returns of a day that had not yet arrived. Of course, before they had another mile behind them, one of Hitler's 'Wolf pack' might strike, or a storm blow up and ships collide perhaps. German bombers were already in the air making for them. There were mines drifting everywhere and if they escaped all these horrors there was always fog, the thick grey-white fog that blinded the whole convoy and made sailing in column a nightmare.

The new second mate had come on watch.

'Nothing special so far,' the Skipper said.

'I'll change your luck I expect,' the Second Mate replied in a biting tone. He had been the sole survivor from a tanker torpedoed in the Irish Sea a couple of months previously. His movements were still a bit stiff and clumsy; he had been rather badly burned and still wore elastic stockings. Just two days after he had been discharged from hospital, he had a visit from people from the shipping office at the Lord Nelson, where he was staying.

'My legs aren't quite right,' he had told them, but the men from the shipping office had brought him elastic stockings and told him he would manage all right if he wore them.

'We're so short of men, appallingly short. We must keep the ships sailing until we beat the Germans,' said the man from the shipping office with the shore job. And the Second Mate felt that it was no use refusing. He just had to go.

Now here he was on the bridge again and in spite of everything glad he had come to a general cargo boat. He did not know whether he could have stood another tanker. He would rather have a few thousand tons of TNT and munitions under his feet. Better to be blown to smithereens than burned, he thought.

Several other tankers had been torpedoed that time before his own was hit. An explosion, a thundering sea of flame, masses of smoke, men burning and screaming. They had had four thousand tons of petrol below decks and they had just gone about waiting for the explosion. It was not the officers but the men who had the worst of it. Two of the men aft had gone off their heads with terror after the U-boats had been harrying the convoy day and night for some time. They had wandered round the crew's mess and cabin corridors singing hymns, only odd lines and half verses of course, because they had scarcely seen a hymn book since they were confirmed. When they were not singing, they recited bits of prayers in loud voices and cried to the others:

'It's our turn now. Death is near! The hour is at hand!'

One of the two had a habit of pressing his front teeth over his lower lip in moments of stress, and after he went off his head he bit his lower lip almost to pieces. It was quite ragged and bloody when the torpedo eventually hit them.

The others had all stood up to it. The Second Mate had been stationed aft and the Captain had ordered him to shut the two crazy men in the sick bay to stop them sending the others off their heads with their hymns and prayers and prophecies of doom. But the deck-hands and engine-room personnel had said that they could stand it and that it would be inhuman to shut the two up in a cabin and so perhaps deprive them of the tiny chance of survival there might be if they were on deck when the torpedo struck. Anyway, they were all dead now, all except him.

The Second Mate had refused to wear his life-jacket, for he was pretty spry and reckoned that he might have a slight chance if he swam under the surface, which would be covered with blazing petrol; so, when the torpedo hit them, he had been on the wing of the bridge and he had dived into the sea, gone deep under and come up where the surface was still free of flame. But thousands of tons of blazing patrol were pouring from the riven tanker, and he had to dive again and swim on under various patches and streaks of water that were alight.

Then the rivers of petrol had united behind him and came hissing after him like a prairie fire. From underneath he had looked up at a roof of flame and swum until it had felt as if his lungs were on fire. When he felt on the point of losing consciousness, he surfaced. He was all but out of the area of flame. His head was and so were his shoulders, arms and back, just beyond the line of fire, but when he kicked out forcefully to get right out into cold grey-green sea, his feet, legs and knees had got burned . . .

Anna was sailing right in the wake of the boat ahead of her. The new Second Mate registered automatically that her speed was what it should be. Everything in *Anna* told of experienced seamen handling her, and the Second Mate suddenly felt at home. He had already seen enough of the Skipper and First Mate to feel that they amply fitted the bill, and the crew looked all right too. He glanced again at the wake of the ship ahead and thought that the lad at the wheel there seemed to know his job all right too.

Before the war *Anna* would have been what is called a 'happy ship', but such a term was meaningless in convoy work. At least the ship was still afloat and he understood that most of her crew had been in her a long time, some since before 1940 and the Chief since her maiden voyage a few years after the end of the First World War.

The westerly wind was increasing and the eighty-one ships of the convoy rolled and pitched their way into the sunset. Hulls creaked, stays hummed, clatter came from the galleys, tarpaulins flapped and the deck-hands were everywhere – for'ard, aft and midships – preparing the ships for bad weather.

In *Anna* the Carpenter was finishing his daily inspection of lifeboats and rafts. The Bo'sun had a mania for seeing that the rescue-gear was in order, but the two made their rounds at different times; thus lashings, disengaging gear, oars, water tanks, provisions, first-aid boxes were all checked – twice. Nothing was ever overlooked, but even so the First Mate also went round making sure that everything was as it should be.

Donkeyman had done himself so well with drink and women in Liverpool that at supper he was half asleep and nodding over his plate; but the Boy, who had just finished a trick at the wheel, was talkative and friendly. He told them about the Skipper's cigarette.

'He's gone funny in the head, too, you'll see,' Donkeyman grunted.

'Perhaps he was sorry for the ticking-off he gave me before we sailed,' the Boy said, feeling rather big; but the moment he had said that he became tongue-tied, just as he did when he let out one of the ghastly oaths he had learned from the impossible Greaser who had disappeared in Liverpool. There was such a nice expression in the Skipper's eyes, when he came up holding out his cigarette-case . . .

'How's that brown-eyed girl of yours?' the Bo'sun asked AB. Somehow the Bo'sun did not like them discussing the Skipper behind his back.

'The wife's just putting her to bed at this very moment,' AB replied, but the words came slowly, almost reluctantly, and he did not go on.

'Seems to me she's a bit crotchety this evening,' the Bo'sun said, for he wanted to have something to take their minds off the convoy. He looked at AB expectantly, but AB sat silent, lost in his own thoughts, until suddenly he said:

'Do you think a ship goes right to the bottom when it sinks, even of the Atlantic?'

The jaws of the men at the table stopped moving. The Carpenter spoke first. 'I've often thought about it,' he said, wrinkling his forehead, 'and I believe that at great depths the pressure is so great a ship just lies there drifting with the deep currents.'

'Obviously a wreck'll go right to the bottom!' Bo'sun said, slightly irritated, shoving his cup from him. Once again he could see his own corpse drifting on a current deep down where no living soul could be.

He was lying horizontal, his hair pulled out by the current and looking like a ragged brush; his trousers and shirt were black and his feet bare and white, as white as his face and hands, like marble. He did not sink, he did not rot, he did not rise to the surface, he just drifted along in the great, cold, dark depths.

The Boy had forgotten all about the Skipper and the cigarette. In a low, rather stammering voice, he said: 'Is it true that there are extraordinary fish in the depths of the Atlantic?'

'Supposed to be some with horrible heads and teeth as sharp as needles and eyes like lamps. There are others like octopuses that paralyse their prey with a sort of electricity,'

AB said. His voice was hoarse and heavy.

Donkeyman had now woken from his dreams of women and foaming beer mugs and heard the last few sentences. Before taking a gulp of coffee, now cold in his cup, he said: 'All nonsense!'

Bo'sun smoked and said nothing, but the Boy stared open-mouthed at AB. *Anna* was beginning to pitch and they could hear the rising wind howling across the deck. A cabin door banged and they jumped at the hard sound of it. The light in the mess had suddenly become glaring and ugly. They found they did not want any more to eat; they just sat tense, looking down at the table. Donkeyman gave a little cough to make some sound and *Anna* rose and fell, rose and fell each time a little farther from the coast and farther out to sea. It would be another twenty days before they reached the other side; and somewhere were the U-boats, and beneath them the great, cold, dark depths and the monsters with dreadful heads and teeth as sharp as needles and eyes like lamps.

Donkeyman coughed again and in an unnaturally loud voice said:

'Wonder if they've got that motor boat repaired at home? They ought to have spruced her up . . .' Then in a more normal voice he went on: 'Fool I was to spend all my money in Liverpool. I should be saving up for a new boat.'

The others nodded and began to feel better.

'Looking old she was. I shall save up for a new one. I'll buy a new one if I get home, you'll see.'

They were looking at Donkeyman gratefully now, but afraid of another silence, so as soon as Donkeyman fell silent, AB took over and began telling them how he must have his house repainted. 'I must have new wallpaper in the kid's room. One of those with fairy-tale pictures, so that she's got something to look at if she wakes before the wife and I on a Sunday morning. You know, nice pictures with gnomes and cows and billy-goats.'

Now they no longer heard the howling of the wind and AB went on telling them what he was going to do, and how the girl would lie, was lying now babbling away in her cot, looking at the pictures on the wall, while AB and his wife lie in bed – and how there was a bump in the eiderdown over her breasts and her long hair was black against white pillowcase. But Donkeyman still had the taste of stale drink in his mouth and he no more wanted to hear about AB's girl than to confess to a priest.

An hour later, when *Anna* was yet farther out to sea, nearer to the U-boat area, the Carpenter said encouragingly: 'It's not so dangerous when we're in ballast. The Germans want fully-laden ships on their way back to England.'

'I wouldn't mind giving up this to-ing and fro-ing between Lime Street and Court Street whether in ballast or not,' said Donkeyman.

'Wouldn't mind knocking off sailing altogether,' Carpenter said.

'If everyone stopped sailing, it would be the end of the whole war. If we didn't carry tanks and planes, bombs, guns and petrol, the army wouldn't have anything to fight with,' AB said.

'Then Hitler could murder to his heart's content,' said Bo'sun.

'True enough,' AB muttered, 'but I'd like to get home alive.'

'Oh, stop that talk,' Bo'sun said. '*Anna*'ll be all right and if not, she's in ballast and we've got lifeboats. The hell of it is though, your wages stop the moment the ship's below the surface.'

'That's because the bloody office pen-pushers think sailing in a lifeboat's a holiday,' the Carpenter said.

In Liverpool they had been given some copies of a news-sheet published by the Norwegian Government in Sweden, and Bo'sun thought this a suitable moment to read out the account of a speech a Norwegian politician had made in London on the subject of the men in the merchant fleet. It was a good speech and Bo'sun had not read many lines before the scornful comments stopped.

There they sat, rather embarrassed, hearts filled with gratitude, listening to Bo'sun's voice telling them how courageous they were to defy U-boats and bombs, mines and storms. All the same they were rather surprised that anyone could find what they did so admirable. Donkeyman was so impressed that he interrupted Bo'sun with a 'Lot of nonsense!'

Bo'sun pretended that he had not heard and read on. The politician had said that the Norwegian seamen would be remembered always for their heroism, and here the Boy interrupted asking what 'heroism' was.

'Same as "fine show",' the Donkeyman told him and the Bo'sun read on. The speech ended with a promise that each Norwegian seaman would be well rewarded when the war was over.

'Lot of nonsense!' Donkeyman exclaimed again. He was provoked by the eloquence of this speech, which had been made at some banquet in London.

Anna was pitching in the high seas that came rolling in from the west, hissing as they came to break on her quarter. Each one lifted her up, canted her over to port and down at the bows, then she righted herself in the trough and was given another powerful shove by the next wave and surged forward, making a bow-wave like a huge white ploughshare.

The eighty-one ships in the convoy rolled and pitched in monotonous rhythm. Their rising and dipping, heeling over and righting themselves again, shaking their sterns and butting their bows was like an oceanic ballet. But all the time they kept station, a compact group, yet far enough apart to avoid collision. The retired naval officer who was now the convoy's Commodore led his flock like some marine *maître de ballet* into the night at seven knots. He would allow no ship to be out of its station because this could lead to catastrophe. The helmsmen stared their eyes out keeping the ships in a line, and the skippers and mates were for ever telling their engine-rooms to increase or reduce speed by a couple of revolutions so that the ships were all sailing at exactly the same speed.

Then, out on the port wing of the convoy, one of the escort vessels began dropping depth-charges. The dull explosions knocked against the sides of the ships, like the drum-beats in the sea's symphony.

The last signal from the Commodore's ship before darkness fell was grim and familiar: 'Enemy submarines are known to be in the vicinity.'

The Skipper liked the weather. Of course, people had different ideas as to what weather suited U-boats best and he knew that a lot of people thought they were most dangerous in rough weather, because then it was more difficult to spot a periscope and impossible to see a torpedo's track; but the Skipper knew that U-boats could attack in all weathers. On their way back to England in the last convoy the sea had been almost dead calm.

He, at all events, was glad that it was rough. There was just enough wind and sea to make *Anna* roll, enough for the crew to have to keep an eye on the way she was behaving – and that was certainly better than a calm when you heard only the monotonous hum from the engine-room, the gurgling of water along the sides, and the steady hiss of bow-wave. All the familiar sounds made quietness more profound and the darkness more intense.

There was no alert, despite the fact that depth-charges had been dropped on the left wing of the convoy. They were now in waters where the Germans had sunk countless Allied ships, and the Skipper thought it probable that the escort vessel had mistaken wreckage for a U-boat. Even so, he preferred to stay on the bridge all night, trying to take an occasional cat-nap in the chart-house.

AB had the first watch, and when he took over from the helmsman at midnight he moved his feet about until he had found the right amount of straddle to meet the movement of the ship. He could see the dark shape of the Skipper on the bridge in front of him. He could also just make out the shapes of the ships on either beam, and the stern of No. 35, the ship next ahead, which he was required to follow.

There was a faint glow from the compass in the binnacle; otherwise it was pitch dark. No light of any sort must be visible. A single porthole not blacked out might bring the destruction of fifty ships. The light from a fifteen-watt bulb can be seen a mile away at sea, and so could cost the lives of hundreds.

Wheel over to starboard, over to port, this way then that, to counter the effect of the seas and keep *Anna* on her course.

A few more depth-charges exploded far out to port and AB felt grateful to the Navy for the tireless watch they were keeping.

The Skipper was silent, and AB turned the wheel this way and that, trying to concentrate on the steering; but he felt the old torpedo horror beginning to mount in him. It came from below, from the deck, from the bowels of the ship, from the deep under the ship. He could feel it in his feet and legs, then it crept up into his belly, was clutching at his stomach, squeezing round his heart causing a heavy ache in his chest, and drying up his throat and mouth. With anxious eyes he glanced at the Skipper, but the dark figure stood as before, staring out into the night.

AB would have given his right arm to hear a human voice, a finger for every word, but as no one spoke he tried talking to himself silently: 'There's no alert, no alert, no alert, no alert, alert, no no . . .' The voice in his head was so loud that he thought the Skipper must be able to hear it; but the Skipper's back was as square on to him as before. Then AB started on the grotesque game he had played with himself on hundreds of watches when at the helm, on look-out, manning the gun or machine-gun. He might have called it the 'shall-I-live-or-die' game. But he had no name for the game in which he imagined a torpedo striking *Anna*, and decided what he should do if this happened.

There were so many possibilities when they were in ballast, as now. Plans differed according to whether the torpedo struck aft, amidships or for'ard. For example, would the Skipper have time to order him to leave the wheel or would the Skipper be killed instantly and so leave the decision to him?

Again AB stared at the dark shadowy shape on the bridge in front of him and hoped that the Skipper's physical presence would help him to collect his thoughts and concentrate on his plans, but he could no longer control them.

Fear got the upper hand again and made him review the catastrophes he had witnessed: ships sinking, exploding, blown sky high, ships sinking, men shouting, bleeding, dying and drowning. AB shook his head, waggled it from side to side, rubbed his knuckles against his forehead and his eyes, and stared ahead towards No. 35. Then he glanced hurriedly at the Skipper, trying to rid his eyes of those inner visions. He stared out into the night and the sea, then looked down at the compass in the binnacle with the yellowish glow of its shaded light. But even that faint light flared up in his mind to become the yellowy, sky-licking tongue of flame from the Norwegian tanker in the previous convoy. All roaring thunderous flame from stem to stern. Men diving into the sea, falling like blazing torches into the sea that itself was blazing because thousands of tons of petrol were gushing out of the torn sides.

And there were the others who were no longer human, burning at the rail, burning then clambering madly up the rigging which was itself burning. AB stared wildly into the darkness; it seemed as if the Skipper's figure was outlined in yellow flame against the night beyond the glass.

But now he heard the figure speaking, heard it shout out loud: 'Watch your steering! Port your helm!' And as the flames in AB's mind subsided, the Skipper was standing shaking him by the shoulder and saying in a fierce voice: 'Do you want to destroy us all, you idiot?'

Anna was back on the right course. The Skipper's rage had jerked AB from his nightmare and now he felt calmer. He began his 'shall-I-live-or-die' game and steered carefully while he planned what he would do if *Anna* was hit.

He saw himself dashing down the ladder on to the lower bridge. The ladder had fourteen steps in it and he had got it into his head that if he could manage ten of them before the next explosion he would survive and be rescued unhurt. If he managed only eight he would also survive, but be disabled; but if he managed less than eight he would be killed. From the lower bridge to the upper deck were twelve steps, but it was only the bridge ladder that mattered. Thus, if no one was looking, he used to practise sliding down the rail beside the ladder, trying to reach the deck as swiftly as possible.

The Chief was asleep. Bo'sun was asleep. The Boy was having a nightmare about the ghastly monsters in the deeps. The others with watch below lay awake, turning and tossing in their bunks, taking a few pulls at their cigarettes then stubbing them out again, trying to think of other things than torpedoes and death, yet keeping their ears pricked for any unwelcome sounds in the night: creaks, thuds, steps on deck, doors being opened and shut, and again the slap of an extra large wave against the ship's side.

The Carpenter woke at about three and his bunk creaked under him as he reached for his packet of cigarettes. From force of habit he looked to see if the cabin hook was in position and the wooden wedge firmly under the door. He lay on his back thinking of what the Bo'sun had read out in the mess that evening, the report of the speech made by the Norwegian politician at a banquet in London. He thought particularly of how the man had said that the seamen were to have their rich reward once the war was over. For the really young, like the Boy, there would be good opportunities, if they survived. They could still go to college or school. For himself, the Carpenter hoped he might be given a job with the harbour board, or as a lighthouse keeper. The idea of the latter he found the more tempting. He would be up there at the top sending shafts of light speeding out across the sea. He often dreamed of this at night on these convoys. It was good to think of it in the vast darkness when the blacked-out ships tried to sneak through waters where packs of U-boats lay waiting for them. He would concentrate on sitting up there at the top of his lighthouse sending long beams of light across the sea. He would sleep by day and with the bonus he would earn by that he would get himself the biggest and softest bed that money could buy. It would be wide enough for him to lie outstretched across it.

And he would not have an alarm clock; that would remind him of the alert-bells on convoy-ships. He would have a wife who would wake him by laying her hand on his shoulder. Then he would fling his arms round her and pull her down into the enormous bed, and he would laugh a lot and she would laugh a lot with him.

And at night, if he was sitting up there alone in his lighthouse, she would be sleeping peacefully. And her sleep would be different from that of other wives, because she would know that he was up there and lord and master of the light and taking care of her and of the ships.

And when his nocturnal watch was over and the ball of the sun had thrust itself above the horizon and mounted into the flushed eastern sky, he would go down to her. He would walk quietly and make coffee and take it into the bedroom, would drink it and smoke and keep quiet, just watching her sleeping there unafraid. And he would look out of the window at a sea bright with sunshine and at white ships crewed by men whose lives would be no longer in danger.

Then he would look down at her again in their enormous soft bed. She would be wearing a pretty nightdress and he would tuck the eiderdown round her for the pleasure of seeing her smile happily in her sleep. He would bring her coffee when she woke and he would tell her about the ships with their bright lights he had seen that night.

Then he would go to sleep – in a bed, in a room, in a lighthouse, on an island off a coast – and there would be nothing to harm him while he slept.

The U-boats often attacked in the grey of the dawn, and that was the hour when the sharpest watch was kept on the eighty-one bridges of the ships in that convoy. In that hour of transition between night and day the ships ploughed on across the Atlantic reminding the Skipper of a herd of elephants he had once seen rolling across the African bush.

Breakfast was being prepared in eighty-one galleys and eighty-one ship's carpenters were sounding the bilges and tanks to check that all was normal.

The Commodore's instructions were that course was to be changed at seven o'clock, at which moment eighty-one ship's officers gave their helmsmen identical orders.

As was his custom *Anna*'s Bo'sun went to the First Mate up on the bridge to be told the day's jobs and then allocated them among the deck-hands during breakfast in the mess.

The Carpenter reported the result of his soundings to No. 1 and wrote them up on the board at the entrance to the engine-room. It was his day for sharpening the galley knives and he wanted to get that done before he set about overhauling the locks of the midship cabins. Now, as he sat having his final cup of breakfast coffee, seven bells was struck and the new Second Mate was roused. He started the day cursing his burns and elastic stockings and by the time he reached the officers' mess he was already worrying about the fact that evening would come again, and then night, and then darkness which made the silent enemy invisible. By day there was at least a slight chance of seeing a periscope or torpedo track; at least there was a chance of seeing when they were going to die and how . . .

When eight bells was struck those who had been on watch since four o'clock that morning came to the mess for a meal. When it was their watch below most would go and lie down on their bunks, because this convoy had not yet been attacked. All that day they sailed in peace and by the next morning they had put another 168 miles between themselves and Britain.

On their fourth night at sea the alarm bells rang in all the ships. Hundreds of electric bells sounded, filling corridors, messes, engine-rooms and wheelhouses. Below deck men leaped from their bunks and, either wearing a life-jacket or with one clutched in a hand, dashed through the blacked-out curtains at the end of the corridors and out on deck.

Several thousand men, British, Greek, Norwegian, Danish, American and Dutch, ran thus to their posts on poop, boat-deck or bridge. Those who had been in their cabin or in the mess were blinded when they dived out of the light into darkness. They staggered across the deck with hands out-stretched, feeling their way by hatches and rails, door- or window-frames, bulwarks, ladders and masts. The wind had increased and spray was flying above their heads as they crossed the slanting deck. The Skipper looked at his watch. It was ten minutes past midnight.

A sharp explosion sounded on the port wing; a bright light flashed. The first victim was in flames. A gun was firing continuously. Such rapid fire could come only from one of the escort vessels. It must have found a U-boat within range.

Depth-charges boomed and the wind howled across the foaming sea, while the hunted ships rose and dipped, rolled and pitched, maintaining the same course and the same speed as before the attack.

The Carpenter and the six others of the gun-crew were at their posts round the old twenty-five-pounder. The Bo'sun had released the safety-catch of the machine-gun on the wing of the bridge. AB was at the wheel and the Boy was look-out. The Chief was at his post in the engine-room. The Skipper knew that his crew were at their emergency stations and had every confidence in them.

It would be fourteen days before those who were to survive reached the other side. More than fourteen days with this weather and the U-boats, for once they had found a convoy they would not let go. A terrible feeling of hopelessness came over the Skipper at the thought of the days and nights ahead of him, of the aching weariness that would be in every cell of his body after days and nights on the bridge – waiting, waiting, waiting for the torpedo that sooner or later must hit his ship. The ripping sound – like a diamond cutting glass – the explosion, and then . . .

Once more he felt the yearning for death that had filled him that night when Liverpool was being raided. He wanted *Anna* to be hit now by her torpedo and get it over. He was almost anxious for it to find his ship, so that there should be no more tiredness, no more alerts, no painful staring at the water for days and nights on end, no more burning ships – just the end, just nothing.

The Skipper stood staring into the darkness. On all the ships men were staring into the darkness and listening to the booms of exploding depth-charges.

Then a ship in the starboard column was hit and the Skipper reckoned that she must have got hit in her bunker-tanks, for the flames were like flood-lighting. From *Anna* they could see hatch covers being flung into the air, half a lifeboat soaring away across the deck, masts crumpling and the funnel going over to one side.

They did not see any other ship go down that night, but they heard explosions in many directions and the hectic activity of the escort vessels left no one in doubt that the U-boats were still attacking. When morning came there were gaps in several of the columns, so that the ships astern of those lost had to increase speed until they filled the gap and all were sailing 'close up' once more.

The Carpenter had been lying down in his survival-suit on the messroom floor for a couple of hours. He had just turned the suit down to his waist so that it did not make him too hot or sweaty, but acted as a mat. Now he slipped it over his shoulders again and stamped out on deck. The ladder creaked under his weight. His tread was heavier than usual because the boots which formed part of the survival-suit were lead-lined. He wore his life-jacket under this rubber suit, so that if he landed in the water the lead-lined boots would make him float upright. However exhausted he was, the survival-suit with its hood and life-jacket underneath would prevent his ever lying with his mouth and nose under water longer than for a moment or two.

If *Anna* was on a return voyage, laden with bombs and high explosives, the Carpenter did not bother to wear his survival-suit. But when she was in ballast there was a good chance of surviving unless you happened to be in the part of the ship where the torpedo hit. The only other thing was to be careful the rubber suit did not get torn during the few desperate moments before you got clear of the sinking ship. That was a thing that could easily happen if you were torpedoed at night and had to run across a deck which the explosion had transformed into a chaos of broken masts and derricks, shattered scuttles, twisted steel plates and splintered planks. One small hole was enough to turn the survival-suit into the opposite, because then it filled with water and you sank like a stone.

So the Carpenter was careful when working in his survival-suit and he took care to empty his bowels as often as possible, for he had heard of a man who had been in the water a long time being hauled aboard with his survival-suit full of excrement and urine. He had a horror of the same thing happening to him, so he ate coffee-beans and prunes to make him go often.

He sounded the tanks and went about his other routine jobs to the tune of depth-charges exploding in the distance. When he entered the mess most of those who had watch below were sitting at the table. They reckoned that the U-boats might attack again at any moment and wanted to be near the boat-deck.

Later in the afternoon, the alarm bells rang again. There was an explosion ahead of them. No. 31 had been hit. Her deck was only just above water when *Anna* drew level with her. There was not a soul visible, but her whistle was wailing unceasingly. The lanyard must have got caught up and there was still steam to keep the whistle complaining. The moment the superstructure and funnel disappeared it was as if the ship sighed, a long heavy sigh that lasted until the mast-tops disappeared.

After dinner the Chief wrote up his log, as was his habit, and smoked a couple of pipes in the officers' mess. Since then he had been in the engine-room, and during an attack he was there pretty well day and night.

Things had hotted up now and the bang of the sound-waves from the depth-charges striking the ship's sides was at times so violent that it might have been a torpedo hitting her. *Anna* creaked and shook under the strain, but the Chief stayed where he was, stooping and peering, but all the time listening to his engines. He heard the least rattle or squeak, even if it was so slight none of the others noticed it. But the old Chief would. He seemed to listen with more than just his ears.

The Second Engineer and the new Greaser trotted to and

fro. They would say nothing for long periods at a time, and when they did speak it was incoherent, and so quick you could not possibly catch a word. Now and again the Second Engineer became so jittery that he disappeared to the back and stayed there, alone and invisible, until he had taken enough control of himself to reappear.

'I'm so old that I don't need sleep,' the Chief said as he came below on the Second Engineer's watch. And when No. 37, the ship behind them in the column, was torpedoed, the Chief pulled out his silver pocket watch. He kept this in a pocket in his waistcoat and had it on a black strap long enough for him to lift it up to his short-sighted eyes. Slowly and deliberately he returned it to its pocket; then he cut a piece of tobacco off his roll and with his thumb put it in position between his gum and upper lip.

The Second Engineer had turned his back to him, but even the Chief's dull eyes could see that the man was trembling. It was just past seven o'clock, so he had almost an hour of his watch left. The Chief cleared his throat and said to his second-in-command that as things were so lively it would be a good idea if he went up on deck to watch what was going on. 'You can stand at the top of the ladder and call down the moment there's anything special,' he said.

The Second Engineer turned only half-way towards him, so that the Chief should not see his eyes. He knew that it was quite pointless for him to be up on deck to call a warning to the others. In ninety-nine cases out of a hundred the torpedo would be through the ship's side before the men could get up the ladders and out on deck; but the urge to get out of the engine-room, which was a death trap, was so overwhelming that he could not bring himself to make even the mildest protest. He just nodded as if it was an ordinary order he had been given and forced himself to climb up slowly, fighting to preserve his dignity. And he did manage to stop himself making a wild scramble up to the fresh air of the deck.

When Donkeyman came on watch at twelve o'clock the Chief went up for coffee and a sandwich. Donkeyman went round seeing that everything was as it should be, but every time a depth-charge exploded close to *Anna* he went rigid and stood motionless for a few seconds. It always seemed to get worse when he left the deck and went below. He could not even conjure up the mental picture of the Liverpool girl or the others in many ports of whom he had pleasant memories. He tried his old entertainment of reckoning out how many women he had been with, but now names and countries and colour of skin and age all got mixed up. When yet another depth-charge went off so close that it felt as if *Anna* hopped up on to the next wave, Donkeyman folded his hands round the manœuvring valve, so that he looked very attentive and conscientious while he prayed.

He realized with a certain satisfaction that he now could say more than just 'Dear God . . . dear God . . . dear God.' He prayed a proper prayer and repeated it because he thought it sensible and modest. 'Dear God,' he prayed silently, 'don't let a torpedo come into the engine-room. Let us have it in the forepeak or, best, in the fresh-water tank, because then we shall have a chance . . .'

Then it struck him that if God was all-powerful and all-knowing, it was perhaps a bit insulting to tell Him that it was best for *Anna* to be hit in the forepeak, and that the fresh-water tank was for'ard. But even so he could not stop repeating it once more so that perhaps God would divert the torpedo a little before it actually hit *Anna* – if it must.

At the last violent explosion, the new Greaser dropped what he was holding and was half-way up the ladder before he came to his senses. He now came down again rather shamefacedly, having to walk across to Donkeyman to demonstrate that he was all right and on the job. He asked for a light for his cigarette and Donkeyman handed him his box of matches, but his hands were trembling so violently that the match went out before he had managed to get his cigarette lit. He twisted the corners of his mouth outwards and thrust his chin forward to produce what was supposed to be a manly smile. His face reminded Donkeyman of a mask he had seen somewhere in the East, and all at once Donkeyman twisted his mouth in the same comical way and thrust out his own small, unimpressive chin. He let go of the manœuvring valve and sticking his thumbs into his ears waggled his fingers.

For a moment the Greaser was so furious he could have smashed Donkeyman's head in, if he had had a spanner in his hand, then all at once his fear melted away and he began to smile, and finally burst out laughing. Encouraged by his success, Donkeyman stuck his little fingers into the nostrils of his snub nose, keeping his thumbs still in his ears, and peals of laughter rang out among the pistons, rods, pipes and shafts. And for quite a number of minutes Donkeyman forgot all about Our Lord and almost about torpedoes. He and the Greaser were now in a mood to talk women and drink . . .

An hour before midnight the electric bells began ringing again.

The Chief cut himself a quid and prepared for a long, watchful night. The Skipper got up from the sofa in the chart-house where he had been vainly trying to snatch some sleep. The Second Mate was on the bridge cursing the itching and smarting in his legs and the damned elastic stockings he had to wear. Those who had watch below were in the mess, sitting crouched and ready to make a dash for the boat-deck and jumping at every explosion.

This time the attack was being made from the head of the convoy. But no morse-lamp sent orders from the commodore's ship for a change of course because before the last ships in the convoy could receive the order to change course, which had to be signalled from ship to ship down the columns, they would be where ships were being attacked at that moment. Also, if they were to change course to port or starboard, they might easily run right into a wolf-pack waiting on that side.

It was pitch dark, and the convoy proceeded on its way through the heavy sea. From *Anna*'s bridge you could see glints of red on the waters ahead, gleams from the little lights fixed to the right shoulders of life-jackets so that the men in the water could have a chance of being seen and picked up.

Suddenly there was scarcely one of the red lights to be seen, but the next moment a wave had lifted the wearers out of the trough and made them visible again. Whether they could swim or not did not matter now. The seas were so great that men were raised up by the foaming waves and plunged down again as if they had been dolls. Bo'sun standing beside his gun thought that it must be enough to send you mad being in a sea like that at night many hundreds of miles from the nearest land with only a life-jacket between you and the depths waiting to suck you down, slowly at first, then more and more quickly until your body was caught by the ever-circulating currents away down in the chasms of the ocean. And he could not help them: no one in *Anna* could help the men with the red lamps.

All *Anna* could do was to press on. Every ship had to continue at the same speed and on the same course. The escort vessels might perhaps try to stop and pick up the men in the water, but only perhaps. It depended on the number of U-boats and the extent of the attack – whether one of the naval craft could put its engine-room telegraph to stop or not. But the convoy itself must sail on, and the escort's prime duty was to protect the ships that were afloat.

The men in the water floundered desperately. *Anna* and

several other ships seemed to be coming right at them, but the exhausted men were powerless to avoid them.

The Skipper was standing on the bridge and it seemed to him that he could see, with the despairing eyes of the men in the water, the sharp bows of his ship looming out of the darkness, see the large shape coming nearer and nearer like a steel monster that crushed everything in its path. To have put the helm hard over at night and in that sea would have been to endanger ship and crew – not only *Anna* and her crew but the other ships and their crews. The Skipper looked to starboard and to port for a glimpse of the ships on his either side, but the darkness and the weather were black, impenetrable walls between the columns, and he could only guess where they were. But they were there. They might be larger or smaller than *Anna*, but if he altered course to port or starboard and got the seas on the beam, *Anna* would be forced even farther off course before she could respond and be got back into position. In such weather the Skipper was as afraid of a collision as of U-boats.

The Boy was at the helm. Young as he was, he could be as quick and efficient as any of the other deck-hands. At that moment the Boy was standing almost on tiptoe, every muscle in his body tensed to react instantly to an order. He was an old hand at convoys now and knew that the absolute rule, that ships must sail on even if half the sea was full of red lamps, was not the cynical decision of ruthless military leaders ashore.

The Boy forced his gaze on to the compass to avoid having to see those red glints coming nearer the bows every second, nearer the threshing propellers. He did not want to look again at the sea; and there he stood, taut as a steel spring, knuckles white from the grip of his hands on the spokes, eyes rigidly on the compass.

Was the Skipper going to alter course round them? He

must. The order must come *now*, *must* come. Then they would escape the bows, and the bow wave would push them aside so that they would not scrape along the ship's side and end in the propellers. Just a little bit to starboard, just a little, so that they did not collide with rolling, pitching ships in the next column. Then the Skipper called: 'Twenty degrees to starboard!' The Boy spun the wheel, while he repeated the order in a voice full of excited eagerness: 'Twenty degrees to starboard it is.'

He looked out at the sea and down at the compass and gave the helm a bit more starboard so that there should be the best distance between the poor wretches and *Anna*. Then the Boy glanced for'ard again and the Skipper's voice reached him just as his eyes discovered that *Anna* was ploughing right into another cluster of lights. 'Hard to port!' the Skipper called.

The Bo'sun on the bridge wing beside his gun tried not to look, but his eyes seemed hypnotized by those bobbing red lamps right beside *Anna*'s bows on the starboard side. There were four or five of them. The Bo'sun squeezed his eyes tight shut, but he could not help turning and looking aft. He could see specks of red! They had gone clear of the ship's side and the propellers.

'Hard to starboard!' called the Skipper.

'Hard to starboard it is,' replied the Boy, but *Anna* was only half back on to her proper course when four or five more red lamps suddenly appeared on the crest of a wave directly ahead. They appeared so suddenly, as if popping out of the depths, that the look-out did not have time to shout 'Man ahead!' before the bows drove into them.

From the bridge they saw the red gleams disappear in towards the forepart and the butting, thumping bows diving down into the trough like an avalanche of steel. And again the Skipper saw his ship with the eyes of the men in the water, saw the sharp, chopping stem, the sheer sides which the men kicked at impatiently in an attempt to push themselves clear.

When daylight finally came, the convoy was reformed. *Anna* had to move forward two positions, for both Nos. 31 and 32 had been sunk. Now she had only three ships ahead of her in her column and was roughly parallel with the Norwegian tanker belonging to *Anna*'s Skipper's friend.

All was peaceful during the afternoon and the Skipper went to try to get some sleep. He felt giddy and despondent, for he seemed to be able to stand less, physically, with every fresh crossing he made. Now only two days and nights without sleep was enough to give him the irksome feeling that neither the ship nor the convoy, nor he himself, was real. He could see the columns all right; but in some way it was not he who saw the lines of ships on the stormy sea. He stood in his cabin, feet pressed against the planks, tightened the aching muscles in his legs to achieve contact with the mat, but it was as if he could not feel his legs. He caught himself staring at his feet, then letting his gaze travel up his legs to his knees and so to his waist, in order to convince himself that he was standing on the floor. He talked aloud in order to hear his voice and it seemed to come from so far away that he spoke more quietly in order to get nearer to it.

If only I could get an hour or two uninterrupted sleep, he thought, this nonsense would stop. He went up to the looking-glass and looked at his bloodshot eyes, the shadows under them dark enough almost to be black eyes. He saw the nerve quivering and throbbing under the skin of his cheek, and then he rang for the steward. It was not that he was hungry, but he wanted to be sure that the ringing he heard when he pressed the bell-push was not imagination. He settled himself more comfortably in the armchair in his saloon and stretched out his legs so that his feet were resting on their heels. He wanted to appear relaxed and natural, and at the same time he wished to observe the expression on the steward's face, which would tell him if he looked the same as usual.

When the Skipper rang, the Steward and the Cook had just agreed that they would serve the crew's favourite dish that day. The Cook had always taken a pride in his cooking and never forgot the importance of food to men who were on watch, or came off watch, always at the same places and at the same times, who saw the same faces and suffered from the same horror. So dinner was a particularly important meal. And the Cook was now more thoughtful and inventive than ever before. He had become quite intimate with many of the others on board. He would not say he exactly loved AB and the Carpenter, Bo'sun and the Boy and the Chief; but he often felt the same affection towards them as he did at home towards the family, when everyone was in a good humour and they were all very nice to him.

It had been like that after his collapse on the boat-deck on the way back to Liverpool, when he had come to in the sick bay to find Bo'sun holding his hands, and he had been so afraid and exhausted that he had just wept all the time. None of the others had made a fool of him then, because he had sat in his bunk for hours on end rowing for his life. He had called out and shouted for help, imagining that he was in a lifeboat, and had rowed and rowed with the result that there was no skin left on his right elbow, because he was always banging it against the bulkhead.

He had asked Bo'sun to tell him about it, after he had had several glasses in a bar in Liverpool, for he had no real memory of anything until *Anna* was back in the Mersey. He had a faint recollection of AB and the Carpenter and several of the others coming to visit him in the sick bay and telling him that he must not be afraid, because they were there and would all look after him.

In the bar in Liverpool Bo'sun had said: 'You're not to

feel ashamed or anything like that, Cook. We all think it's damned fine of you not to have asked to be signed off. It's a darned sight nicer in *Anna* with you staying aboard. We're used to your old dog's dinners, you see . . .'

The Cook remembered it word for word. At the same time it had given him such a nice warm feeling and now, as he stood in the galley, he thought that he was 'pretty soft-hearted', for he was in the crew's mess at breakfast time that morning and saw AB, Bo'sun and the Boy and the others with watch below sitting there scarcely able to get one slice of bread down. There they sat thinking; none of them talked and every time a depth-charge exploded away between the lines of ships, they jumped.

The Cook was afraid, too, and he was not the kind of person who could think of something funny to cheer up such a glum mess; but he had the galley and the provisions in his charge and that was why he had had a talk with the Steward and they had agreed on steak for dinner. He searched among his supply of meat until he was sure he had got the best and most tender pieces. Large steaks they were to be, large and with masses of onion. And not 'half done' so that it was all pink and raw inside, but well done, as the men liked it. He was so preoccupied with his steaks that he quite forgot he was at sea. He chopped up onion after onion, wiping the tears away with a corner of his apron.

Bo'sun was to have the largest steak. The Cook put it on its own plate and made an extra flourish with his arm as he sprinkled it with pepper and salt.

Although he had heard of 'stiffening morale' and that sort of thing, such phrases meant nothing to him; but the old saying did, that without food and drink even a hero's not much use.

He ladled onion, crisp and juicy, on to each steak. The smell that filled the galley excited him, as if it was Christmas, and he produced some pickles and four tins of pineapple for the sweet. The inexperienced English mess-boy they had signed on in Liverpool was in his bunk seasick, and the Cook took the food to the after mess himself, cheeks glowing with anticipation, and from the heat of the stove.

There was something about the Cook that, together with the lovely smell, roused the spirits of the men in the mess.

'Christ! Are we anticipating Christmas, Cook?' Bo'sun said, and he gave one of his grunting laughs that he only produced when in a good humour.

The Cook had stuck a serving fork into the largest steak and he saw that the dish went first to Bo'sun, who almost automatically took the piece intended for him. Having achieved that, the Cook sat down on a bench beside the table and lit the end of a cigarette and felt quite 'soft-hearted' as he watched the men wading into the steaks and onion, smacking their lips, chewing and gobbling everything up.

'You can certainly make a fine dog's dinner, Cook,' the Carpenter said with good humour.

Donkeyman was the only one who could not eat with relish. He sat glowering at his plate. Every now and then he did cut off a piece of meat almost automatically, but his jaws were continually stopping, while he stared fixedly either at his plate or at the bulkhead.

Donkeyman's nerves had played up during his last watch. The Chief had told him he could go up on deck for a bit and Donkeyman had fallen into a fury and shouted at the Chief, telling him he didn't think much of him and that it was easy enough for a Chief, who had lived so long, to be killed, etc. And when the Chief had taken no notice, Donkeyman had become quite wild and raged on against the Chief and 'that Jesus of his'. The Chief had looked at him then and tried to say something, but he had not been able to get anything out and had just stood there looking awkward and miserably fumbling with his roll of tobacco.

Donkeyman had made a rush for the after deck, where no one could see him, and stayed there a good half-hour. He had not been able to make himself say he was sorry, but had just stood there wondering desperately how he could put matters right. Just before the end of his watch, he had taken off the little bag he always wore slung round his neck by a cord, a canvas bag in which he kept his seaman's book, passport, family snapshots and a few dollar bills, and had taken it to the Chief and asked him if he would look after it, saying he was quite sure the Chief would come through all right. He also managed to say that he knew he could rely on the Chief, because he had religion. He hoped that this had made up for some of the things he had shouted at him about Jesus.

At first the Chief had not wanted to take the bag, but that had only made Donkeyman more insistent and in the end the Chief had passed the loop over the green celluloid peak of his cap and settled it round his neck. 'You can have it back when we get to the States,' the Chief had said.

Donkeyman went and sat on his bunk. He hated himself because he had gone for the Chief like that. He could not understand how he could have vented his wrath on the nice old Chief. And he regretted having parted with his bag too, and having buttered the Chief up for being a Christian.

When Donkeyman went on watch again the wind had got up and a stiff breeze was blowing with stormy squalls. Heavy seas were breaking over the deck and a flood of water poured from *Anna* like a foaming river every time she rose on to a crest. He had scarcely got to his post in the engine-room before the alert sounded.

There was an explosion out on the port wing and through his glasses the Skipper saw a ship break in two. He wondered whether in those seas they would manage to get the lifeboat into the water undamaged and on an even keel and, as so often before, he calculated what chances they would have in

Anna if the same thing should happen to them.

Now he was alert and energetic again. There were the elements to contend with, and *Anna* needed expert manœuvring if she was not to get out of station. Every time a mountainous breaker flung the ship to starboard, you had to order a few more revs, because if she fell away too much she could quickly find herself several degrees off course. The bows were continually coming up to port, and then the Chief had to reduce speed slightly to prevent *Anna* getting too close to the ship ahead of her. One mistake at the helm, a few seconds' inattention and failure to keep *Anna* into the wind and the seas, might find her flung so far over that they could not get back on to her course before they were dangerously near the ships in the next column.

Anna dug her stem into the deep troughs between the waves, almost burying it, and when she raised herself again it was at first almost hesitantly, then quivering and shaking she rose faster and faster as the weight of water poured off the foredeck. The spray flew up yards into the air and the look-out on the wing of the bridge was continually having to lower his head and rub the salt water out of his eyes.

The Skipper was not worried about *Anna* as long as the rudder chains or some other part of the steering gear did not give under the strain. He did not think of the engines. It had never occurred to him that there could be any serious breakdown below deck when the Chief was there at his post.

Another foaming, greeny-white crest had just lifted up the forepart when there was a loud bang ahead and to port. No. 21 had been hit. It was as if the ship had run into an invisible wall, for she reared up and seemed to be flung backwards; then her bows began to turn to starboard. Nos. 22 and 23 put their helms over to port, but in that wind and sea they were painfully slow in turning and No. 24 was even slower, because she had already been a little off course to starboard when No. 21 at the head of the column was hit. The torpedoed ship drifted faster and faster towards *Anna*'s column.

The Skipper could see that the ships ahead of *Anna* would miss the wreck all right, but that *Anna* would go slap into her if he kept on a steady course. The next ship to port had still not got back on to her course, while the one following *Anna* had already begun to swing to port to pass the sinking ship on the lee side. The American ship behind *Anna* had obviously increased her speed and would shortly be just astern to go up to leeward. If *Anna* went to port now, she would risk a collision, and it would be just as bad if she slowed down.

He chose what seemed to involve the least danger; ordered full speed ahead with the intention of giving a little starboard helm in a moment or two so that *Anna* would pass a short distance to leeward of the torpedoed ship. If she could scrape past really close, she would not end up dangerously near the ships in the next column to starboard, as would otherwise be the case.

The doomed ship was still relatively high in the water, and the wind and the waves took hold of the ten-thousand-tonner and pushed her farther across *Anna*'s course. From *Anna*'s bridge they could see a group of men trying to lower a lifeboat and keep it from being smashed against the ship's side. Now they were so close to the sinking ship that they saw a man suddenly collapse on the boat-deck and lie there until a large wave increased the list and he began to slither down the tilting deck.

The wreck was now fifty yards in front of *Anna* and almost dead ahead. The Skipper ordered thirty degrees to starboard and with wind and waves hammering against her port side *Anna* turned relatively quickly. But a sudden gust sent the wreck along faster than he had calculated. There was the column of ships on the other side and he glanced across at his friend's tanker which was still almost parallel with *Anna*. Frantically his brain calculated drift and speed, then he called: 'Fifteen degrees to starboard.'

The helmsman put the wheel over and *Anna* turned her bows dangerously nearer to the starboard column.

They only just made it. They swept past the sinking ten-thousand-tonner so close that you could almost have jumped from *Anna*'s deck on to the wreck's fo'c'sle. The next thing was to avoid colliding with the ships to starboard, which seemed to have carried on more or less without altering course. But before the Skipper had managed to call 'Hard to port,' those on *Anna*'s bridge heard a howling sound to leeward that was distinct from the roar of the storm and the thunderous crash of breakers. The look-out shouted something or other, and the Skipper caught a glimpse of a torpedo that had leaped clear of the water between two waves and was darting like a rocket into the next wave, heading straight for *Anna* at an angle of ninety degrees.

'It's going to strike our afterpart,' the Skipper said. His voice was flat and unemotional.

The helmsman had gone rigid. He stood there holding the wheel and knowing that a torpedo was coming from the port side, while *Anna* was rolling and pitching at a horribly short distance from the line of ships to starboard.

Suddenly it was as if a gigantic hand had seized the men on the bridge and almost threw them over. An enormous wave had taken hold of *Anna*'s stern and lifted it up, flinging the ship sideways as if she had been a piece of cork. *Anna* plunged forward with such force that there was water over the forepart and well up the bridge structure. Astern, the propellers raced wildly – but there was no explosion.

The torpedo passed under *Anna*'s keel and found another target – the Norwegian tanker that was moving abreast of *Anna*. There was a deafening explosion and a piece of steel came whistling from the exploding tanker and knocked a gaping hole in the starboard side of *Anna*'s wheelhouse.

Anna's bows were still in the trough of a wave. She seemed to be fighting for her life. They could feel her resisting the tremendous pressure on her forepart, but there was nothing they could do. Then they could feel the sea give in. Inch by inch *Anna* righted herself, and the helmsman, who had been trying to remember the Lord's Prayer but had got stuck, hung on the wheel blessing her and talking to her as if she really had been alive. Then the propellers bit again and when they had time to think about the other ships once more, they saw that *Anna* had gone right through the column to starboard of her. She had gone straight through the gap left by the Norwegian tanker that had just been blown to bits. By the time she had righted herself she was half-way between the fourth and fifth columns. The Skipper left her there while he reduced speed then let her fall back until she was right astern at the rear of the convoy. Then he increased speed again and took up position as last ship in the column in which the Norwegian tanker had been.

The giant wave that had saved *Anna* from the torpedo had torn off a couple of ventilators and removed the drum-ends, but otherwise the ship was undamaged. In the engine-room the Chief chewed his quid undisturbedly, while pistons and shafts and valves functioned sweetly and regularly.

The Skipper was silent and more unapproachable than ever; in fact everyone aboard was a bit subdued after the Norwegian ship had been blown up right beside them – for they all knew that her captain had been the Skipper's friend. AB's head hung lower than ever. He had been at the wheel at the time when the greetings had been signalled, and seen how the Skipper had been almost gay. Now he was look-out on the port wing and kept his eyes on the sea all the time. He did not want to look in the Skipper's direction.

There was no discussion of why the tanker had been blown to smithereens. They knew that her crew had not had enough time to clean the tanks properly while they were in England; that the tanker, as so often happened, had been ordered to sea again the moment she had finished discharging. The captain of course would have protested, but would have been given the usual answer: that the need of oil and petrol for the Allied armies and navies and air forces was acute and that tanks could be aired and cleaned at sea. But bad weather and high seas must have put them behind schedule, so that there was still a residue at the bottom of the tanks.

The only thing left of the big tanker was the jagged piece of steel that had gone through the side of *Anna*'s wheelhouse. It was lying on the floor, and when *Anna* was back on course the Skipper walked across, picked it up and took it down to his saloon. He was back on the bridge a few moments later and no one dared speak to him all the rest of the evening . . .

The wind had dropped slightly but the seas were still running high. Most with watch below were sitting in the mess trying to rest, heads pillowed on their arms on the table. One or two were lying on the floor with their survival-suits on, ready to dash out on deck if anything happened.

When he was relieved, Bo'sun left his gun on the bridge and came aft. He had intended to lie down in the mess for a bit, but there was such a fog in there, it was quite difficult to breathe for someone coming off the deck. The place smelled of wet clothing and sour sweat from bodies sealed in rubber survival-suits. Bo'sun stood for a moment hesitating, then he went to his cabin, pulled his rubber suit down to his hips, and flung himself on his bunk with his lead-weighted boots sticking over the edge.

He was feeling deadly tired, but could not get to sleep. He could not stop thinking about those little red lamps on the men in the water, and he kept seeing that last cluster of them into which *Anna* had driven. He shut his eyes but the red lights still shone. At times they were mere specks, then they grew and grew like balloons being inflated. They were there, horizontal and vertical, in his mind's eye; and however tightly he squeezed his eyes shut he still saw them, as if with the back of his eyes, dancing to and fro, flaring up and bobbing about.

He forced himself to lie absolutely still and eventually fell into a doze. But there again were red lights floating in the black nothingness, and it was not long before he woke, pouring with sweat. The dream had been so vivid that he could still hear voices – the cries of the men being tossed about with red lights on their shoulders – even though in actual fact he had not heard a cry when *Anna* ploughed through those great seas and straight in among the poor wretches. No one had. There had been no sounds but those of the wind and the wild breaking seas; but in his sleep Bo'sun had heard the torpedoed men calling out: voices coarse and rough like his own, and clear boys' voices, all shouting the same: 'No! No! No!'

And in his sleep he had called 'no' to them, shouted 'no' with them. 'No! No!' He had been with them in the foaming sea and seen *Anna*'s bows and her high, dark sides thrusting at him and been dragged and rubbed along the keel and thrust in towards the propeller whirling like a black wheel in a cloud of greeny-white foam.

Bo'sun got up and sat on the edge of his bunk, thinking. When he had smoked his fifth cigarette almost to the end, he stubbed it out carefully in his ash-tray and went up to the mess. He had to have someone to talk to straight away.

He had worked hard all his life and considered hard work the natural order of things. He had had to deal with storms and hurricanes at sea, with human sharks ashore, and it had never occurred to him that he could do anything but struggle on until he or his opponents were vanquished. Now, with the red lights still tormenting him, he began trying to devise ways and means of getting the better of the sea, of depriving it of some of its prey, so that he would feel less of a mean hound if *Anna* were to thrust in among any more men from torpedoed ships. It had to be something special, because there could be no question of stopping as long as the ship was in convoy. And as they could not heave to and fish the men out, it would have to be something that caught them up even if *Anna* was sailing at convoy speed. He was pleased to find the Carpenter in the mess and for a long time the two sat there discussing possible methods of rescuing men in the water . . .

By morning the wind had dropped and during the day the seas subsided.

Early that afternoon Bo'sun and the Carpenter were able to make practical experiments to test their ideas. They fetched some coils of rope from the fore-deck and unwound various lengths of the different thicknesses. Then they tied large knots every eight inches so that those in the water could have something to hold on to while they were being hoisted up. Next they had to try to calculate the jerk a man who seized hold of a rope would be subjected to and the strain of being towed along before he could be hoisted up.

AB was the guinea pig. He laid a firm hold of a knot and took up position on the after edge of No. 3 hatch, while the Carpenter clasped his arms round his waist from behind intending to hold him back with the amount of force they thought corresponded to the resistance of the water when *Anna* was sailing at normal speed. Bo'sun and a couple of others took up position five yards or so in front of AB to haul on the rope and pull AB to them. They gave a tug, but only pulled in about a yard of rope, before AB with a yell let go of the rope and stood there, red in the face, cursing his smarting hands.

Donkeyman tried next. Bo'sun was so eager for the experiment to succeed that he scarcely tugged at his end at all, but not even Donkeyman could stand the strain on his palms and arms and he let go just about as quickly as AB had.

Then the Carpenter fetched a broom handle and sawed it

up into suitable lengths, which were lashed to the end of a stout line, in the exact middle of each piece of wood so that it would lie more or less horizontal on the surface and be easy to take hold of. To put this idea to a realistic test they fastened a large bucket to the lowest piece of wood and lowered it over the rail. The moment the bucket entered the water and filled, it was jerked aft so violently that the wood snapped.

Darkness fell and they crowded into the mess, still full of enthusiasm for the Bo'sun's plans, and spent the rest of the evening discussing suggestion after suggestion.

The next afternoon they tried out a rope ladder. Carefully they lowered it until the bottom rung reached the water. The ladder was swept aft but when the wave let go of it, it swung for'ard again with such force that no one could have clung to it. And if you had not had hold of it and it had hit you, it would have knocked you senseless.

They tested other ideas as well, but the results were all equally discouraging. Bo'sun, however, would not admit defeat. He produced a plan for making a big net which could fish men out of the water like fish in a trawl. If they got to New York, he said, he was going to get one of the nets they used in the docks for loading and unloading smaller goods and connect it to the winch . . .

The wind had dropped to a light breeze and later in the afternoon it died away altogether. Then it began to rain, pouring down from low clouds on to the grey ships and shallow, glossy waves. Dusk fell and visibility was bad, and AB was sent forward to the fo'c'sle as look-out. He was so nervy that he kept thinking he saw menacing shadows in the semi-darkness. He had half an hour of his time as look-out left when the last of the light was extinguished on the horizon. AB stared out at the sea. He looked again at his wrist-watch. The luminous hands seemed to have stopped moving and he put the watch to his ear, hoping that it had stopped; but it was still ticking. He stood there with his wrist to his ear and it was a sort of comfort to hear the tick.

It was all right being look-out in the bows during the day, when you could count the waves or pick out a long-crested one well ahead and follow it until *Anna*'s stem cut it in two. By day you could also follow the signals sent from the Commodore's ship if she was near enough, and watch the other ships in the convoy, see the men manning the guns and the mates and skippers pacing up and down the bridge-wings. But at night in the menacing darkness, right for'ard in a boat making her way without a light, merging with the night and the sea, AB was mortally afraid the whole time.

Sometimes he had to press his hand to his mouth and bite on it to suppress the urge to cry out, just to break the silence of the darkness, to hear something other than the sea. This was when the roar and splash of water round the bows turned to voices, voices he knew: his wife's voice, the voice of his mother, the voices of living men he knew, of dead men he had known. The faintly luminous veils of foam on the crests of waves could become white faces, the faces of his nearest and dearest, and that was even more dreadful than when the torpedo-horror was upon him.

The torpedo-horror made his brain whirl: torpedoes would speed in every direction, criss-crossing like logs sweeping down a cataract; but there was a reasonable explanation for this, or so he thought. It was when foam turned into faces that AB feared for his reason.

At last his time was up and he could go up to take his trick at the wheel before he started his watch below. Rain was still pouring down, drumming on the deck and bridge, washing the faces of the look-outs and flattening the seas still further.

Morning came and yet another morning, and when the rain stopped, fog came rolling up. First it came in clouds rolling across the water, and then there would be a clear patch with several miles' visibility before they were enveloped in another mass of fog. The ships round them kept disappearing and re-emerging, seeming larger and closer to *Anna* than they actually were, because they appeared so abruptly and unexpectedly and you suddenly saw the outline so dark and sharp.

Before the fog closed down on them again the Commodore had signalled orders to rendezvous at a certain position at a certain time the following day. The Skipper hated fog more than anything else. There were ships ahead of them, ships astern of them, ships on all sides of them. Even if *Anna* managed to keep to her own course, that would not help him if any of the others got out of station. He could not do anything to save *Anna* then. If a ship turned until she was sailing more or less across the convoy, you might have a sharp stem cutting into you before you had time to give an order.

The Boy was look-out for the time being, and the Skipper prayed that he would not relax for a second, for if they lost contact with the fog-buoy they would lose contact with everything. On foggy nights you could not even see the shadow of another ship in the convoy, and the ships kept together by means of the fog-buoy, which each boat towed behind her on a long line.

That blessed buoy, the Skipper thought. He would have liked to have met the fellow who had invented this simple and effective device. It was a sort of wooden cross that floated with an 'open scoop' as a sort of keel and a piece of piping sticking up over the surface. The speed forced water against the 'scoop' and up the pipe, from which it streamed like a fountain. As long as the forward look-out kept his eye on this jet of water and called out or struck the bell the moment it began to shift to one side or the other, there was no need to worry, however thick the fog was. But if they lost sight of the buoy, they had to fumble blindly and desperately before they found their place in the convoy again.

In previous convoys three ships had got lost, but made contact again. Their skippers had been convinced that they had been in their correct positions, but when daylight and visibility had returned, they had had a shock, discovering that they were in a column far from the one in which they ought to have been. These were lucky ships. Others that lost contact did not always blunder into openings in the other columns; they were as dangerous as floating mines.

The Skipper went into the chart-house for a smoke. He must try to keep calm, to rely on the Boy being able to keep his eye on the fog-buoy.

And the Boy did his best. He squeezed his slender body into the peak until his chest was pressed against the bulwark right up in the bows. He scarcely dared blink, he was so afraid of losing sight of the jet of water a short distance ahead of *Anna*'s sea-worn stem. He was weary, as were all the others – heavy in the head and weak from lack of proper sleep. But he must not lose sight of the buoy. He felt his responsibility as an almost intolerable burden. He knew from his own experience how easy it was to become muzzy-headed and sleepy in fog, and if he felt his attention lessening he would give his own face a slap and turn his head this way and that. There was a cold, clammy draught from the hawse-pipes round his legs, but he was glad of it, because the cold helped him to keep his eyes open.

Then he was relieved and went to take his trick at the wheel; after that he had another spell as look-out, but this time on the wing of the bridge. Throughout the night AB and the others relieved each other in the wheelhouse and as look-out, while in the engine-room Donkeyman and his fellows stood their watches in the same way. They were fortunate and got through the dark hours, and in the morning the wind freshened and swept the fog away.

The Commodore found two ships missing when, later in

the afternoon, the convoy reached the appointed rendezvous. They sailed on for a while at slightly reduced speed to see if the two would catch up, but there was no sign of them. Either the two must have got seriously off course or the U-boats had got them.

The Commodore ordered seven knots' speed again and the convoy proceeded on its way to the coast of America.

PART FOUR

The day they caught the first glimpse of land as a low haze on the horizon, the convoy began to spread, as the ships set off for their different destinations. Some made for Halifax, others for Mobile, Detroit, New Orleans or Baltimore. *Anna* was to go straight to new York and evening had fallen by the time she and a score of others from the convoy were sailing the last few miles of river up to the metropolis.

There was light everywhere: white light from millions of bulbs, yellow lights, red lights, blue and green lights. The men of the convoy was so hungry for light after the black-out in England and their journey that they could not stop staring at a world where there was no terror, no rationing, no black-out curtains, no air-raid alerts or bombed houses. They could not go ashore until the following day, but they had the pleasure of contemplating it all. The moment they had tied up and the hum from the engine-room had stopped, the Steward came aft with two bottles of whisky from the Skipper: one for the deck-hands and one for the men in the engine-room. They were all so exhausted that a couple of big tots was enough to make them tipsy. They said nice things about the Skipper for giving them the whisky, and then they remembered his friend in the tanker that had been blown to smithereens and the birthday celebration the two skippers were not going to have in New York. Again and again they talked of how *Anna* had lifted up her stern just high enough to make the torpedo miss her and those who had been in her a long time could not find words enough to praise her.

The new Greaser, who had signed on in Liverpool, was so moved by their praise of *Anna* that he began to waver in his resolve to sign off in New York. So far he had changed ships as quickly as he could, signing off and on in each port because he thought he had a better chance of survival if he left a ship that had made a crossing unscathed.

'You can't bet on the same number twice running, you know,' was his favourite expression; but after the miracle with that torpedo, even the new Greaser began to regard *Anna* as a very remarkable ship.

'It's because the Chief's got religion, you'll see,' he told the Boy when, later that evening, they were standing by the rail, feeling pleasantly affected by the whisky and the lights and anticipation of the next day's adventures ashore. 'The Old Man's a good fellow, too,' the Greaser added.

'Yes, he's asked me how I am several times; and once the Chief gave me a couple of shirts,' the Boy replied, a serious warm note in his voice.

The two tots had roused Donkeyman's thirst and he now went amidships to test 'the Steward's kindness of heart'; but he came back with a hang-dog expression and the news that there was not a bottle to be had on loan from that 'damned poison-mixer'.

AB and the Carpenter were talking together. Carpenter laid his great hand on the other's narrow shoulder and said there was hope there might be a letter from his wife in New York.

'Several people have had letters from Norway through the Red Cross,' the Carpenter repeated. He was always telling poor AB about this and the possibility of it happening to him; at sea it was one way of getting AB to talk and tell them more about his wife and brown-eyed little daughter.

So far AB had never had a letter in that or any other way, nor did the Carpenter think there would be one waiting for him now in New York; but as long as AB thought it possible, they had more to talk about when in convoy. The disappointment of not finding news from home was not really great, for AB never really dared to believe there might be a letter for him, and anyway all disappointment ashore could be drowned in beer and whisky . . .

AB and Bo'sun had gone with the Chief to the Seamen's Church. On the second day, as they were going ashore, they had seen the Chief standing by the gangway in his dark suit and had decided to go with him. There was good coffee, and a woman sang some Norwegian songs, and afterwards a clergyman spoke, ending briefly with a prayer that God protect seamen against all evil and be with them on their dangerous missions across the sea. Neither AB nor Bo'sun knew what to do with their fists when the clergyman started praying. They sat staring rigidly at the back of the person in the seat in front of them. But the Chief had folded his hands and muttered 'amen' when the clergyman did, a double 'amen-amen' in fact; and he kept his eyes closed and his round-shouldered back bowed forward so that it looked as if he was going to topple over. 'Those were good words,' he said, as they all began straightening up.

It embarrassed the Bo'sun when people folded their hands and prayed aloud, and this plus the fact that he had been in a bad mood because of the failure of his experiments made him answer crossly: 'It's all right for the clergyman to pray for us. That, after all, is his job. But I put more faith in a big escort than in his prayers!'

'At least he means well,' AB said soothingly.

'Well, then, he might ask God to help me find a way of fishing men who have been torpedoed out of the sea,' Bo'sun said even more vehemently and now so loudly that people near them turned round.

'I have asked God to do that,' the Chief said gently.

Bo'sun seemed to shrink visibly, then he thrust his shoulders back and growled:

'Then God must have stopped listening to you.'

The moment he had said it, Bo'sun regretted having done

so, and his sense of guilt made him really furious. Four-square and ruthless he made straight for the exit and for the first available place in which to get drunk. People half-protested as he barged them out of his way. One man said, 'You might look where you're going.' Bo'sun stopped abruptly and, thrusting his face into the other man's, hissed, 'Just say that again!' But the man swallowed and said nothing.

AB kept in Bo'sun's wake and behind came the Chief saying 'Excuse me! Excuse me!' to all who had to move. The Chief was quite out of breath when he caught up with AB on the pavement outside the church. Bo'sun was striding off down the street without as much as a backward glance at his companions. AB made to follow him, but the Chief caught him by the sleeve and asked: 'Have I said anything wrong?'

The Chief looked so helpless standing there, eyes blinking behind the strong lenses of his spectacles, that AB had to give him a pat on the back, and in a firm, kindly voice said, 'No, of course not. Bo'sun's been a bit touchy ever since we ran into those men in the water and none of his rescue ideas worked. You know him, Chief. He always takes on when things don't go right.'

'So it wasn't my fault?' the Chief said, not altogether satisfied.

'Not a bit. You'd even prayed to God to help Bo'sun with his experiments,' AB said, and thought that was a good thing to say and would cheer the Chief up.

'Perhaps it was because of that,' the Chief, said, looking even more depressed.

AB was sorry for him and, feeling thirsty himself, asked if the Chief would not like a cup of coffee or lemonade. 'We can go to a proper, decent place,' he added to tempt the Chief. So when they came to a place that looked 'decent' they went in, and AB drank his beer slowly, which he thought would please the Chief.

After a while the Chief said that he must be going:

Donkeyman was signing off and there was this and that to be done and he must get back on board. AB sat on where he was. After several more drinks, AB began to get tipsy and being on his own made him feel very melancholy. After a few more drinks, the feeling of awkwardness at being by himself in such a posh place vanished and he leaned back in his chair and stared challengingly at the people at the other tables.

Landlubbers! Lot of bloody landlubbers! Not one man in a seaman's jersey; not one mouth singing, not one stout fellow on his feet shouting that the next round was on him, ready to fork out his last cent to provide beer and gin for all thirsty souls present. Here everyone wore collar and tie and had clean-shaven faces and, though they drank and drank, they did not laugh, or weep, or sing. They just raised their glasses and ate and talked to the women they were with – it was all too bloody high class for him. And AB cursed them to himself because they were all so pleased with themselves and had plenty of money and would go home with their women through the brightly lit city and sleep in a bed every night of their lives until they died. He cursed them because they could always walk along streets and go home and put their kids to bed, if they weren't too busy that is.

And he thought of his wife at home and their brown-eyed little girl. It was always more difficult to believe that he really had a little girl when he was alone and this filled him with even more bitterness at the landlubbers who could go home to their kids, and if they did not have one they could go home and to bed and make one.

Many of the people at the tables round about looked displeased. Their voices became peevish if the waiter did not come quickly enough, and they picked at their food as if they suspected it of being bad. AB would liked to have gone to a bar where there were other seamen, but he could not make the effort. He sat there watching the others and was so busy wondering at the fact that all those people were able to be on land all the time and go to bed every night without having to worry about torpedoes, while he had to sail in convoys and wait until he was blown to smithereens.

AB drank glass after glass and became more and more angry and desperate at the injustice of his being the one who should not possess anything but a change of clothes, a worn suitcase and the right to use a narrow bunk in a cramped cabin. He was the one who had to go to sea, who was probably going to be killed – not they with their flats and houses and deep armchairs and bedrooms and children and firm ground under their feet all day and every day, while his home, his world, were merely two or three square yards of floor in a cabin. He had to sail off and be killed for people like those round him, who wouldn't look at him, who picked at the fine grub on their plates and who wouldn't join in a round.

AB was so preoccupied with his bitter thoughts that he forgot to speak English and ordered a fresh drink in Norwegian. A man who had just sat down at a nearby table looked up interestedly from the newspaper he had in his hands and said, 'Hallo, Norway!'

The man was a very talkative Norwegian American, and while AB just contributed an occasional 'yes' or 'no' to the flood, the other gave his opinions about the 'old country', the war, the Germans and Churchill. AB wanted peace, wished the other to hell out of it, so he just sat there silent except for an odd yes or no, smoking and drinking and trying to find an answer to the incomprehensible problems of life exemplified by himself and the others in the restaurant.

The other, however, interpreted his silence as interest and moved across to AB's table. After that AB really had to listen to what the man was saying. In an excited voice he was protesting against the dreadful war and the ghastly taxation the government had imposed on business. He himself was making ten thousand dollars a year, but he had to pay more than two thousand in taxes to 'that damned socialist, Roosevelt'.

Then AB began to talk. The bitterness in him welled up into words and he spoke for all the men in *Anna*, and in all ships in all convoys.

'To hell with you,' he said. 'To hell with you and your dollars and your whining. Taxes, you say,' he glared furiously at the American. 'Taxes! I pay tax on the lousy £20 a month I get in wages. I pay taxes for the pleasure of lying in a narrow bunk or on the bare deck waiting to be killed by a torpedo. I pay seventy-five shillings a month for what some authority in London calls a 'saving bonus', something we're to get when peace comes. But who's going to get what we save, do you think? Do you think I will? Do you think any of us will get our money? Any of the seventy-five bloody bob of my wages they take every month? Do you think we can escape a torpedo much longer with ships being blown up and sinking every time we cross the Atlantic? Then there's something called 'allotment' for one's wife in Norway, so the authorities say. Do you think my wife and child will ever get it? Do you think they have bread every day in Norway now?'

The American became solemn and a red flush was growing up his neck and over his cheeks to his forehead and his thin hair that was parted at the side. But AB no longer saw him. He was unburdening himself of years of fear, loneliness and longing. He was speaking for Bo'sun, the Boy, Carpenter, Donkeyman, the Skipper and the Chief, for the whole lot of them.

'You complain about taxes, you landlubber! Well, you can change with me if you think life's too hard here. Change with me. Take my job in *Anna*. Spend your days at sea being frightened to death. Change places with me, if you've so much to complain of here ashore. You said you wore yourself out with work. OK, change with me. You'll get time off. We're entitled to one day off for every month's sailing in convoy. Did you hear? We're entitled to twelve days off a year. Twelve days ashore for facing death on the other three hundred and fifty-three. Change places with you, I'll dance with joy if I can have every other Sunday off.'

The American beckoned to the waiter. AB no longer saw him. He went on in a loud voice:

'You take my job on board, you and all your politicians and businessmen and merchants who say sob-stuff nice things about us on Norway Day – feet on firm ground while they talk a lot of balls, and then go home to houses that can't sink and eat and belch and are given medals for speaking so beautifully about us seamen.'

The American had gone. He had gone back to his own table and was beckoning to the waiter energetically. He was hurt. More than that, he was mortally offended. He had been prepared to devote some of his time to this vulgar sailor because he was Norwegian. He had joined him at his table and spoken sympathetically to him and all the thanks he had got was to be slandered, almost assaulted.

The waiter had come and gone again, and now the head waiter came hurrying up, alarmed and apologetic. The American felt a bit better when he saw the sailor being refused further service and asked to leave.

AB had shouted those last few sentences and people had looked up in fear and horror at this skinny figure with the great head who had dared to come into such a respectable place. Now he got to his feet, flung a dollar bill on the table for a tip, and walked between the lines of tables towards the door, but he never saw the men and women who put down knife and fork to enjoy the sight of someone being turned out. All AB saw was *Anna* and the men he sailed with and the sea. Out on the pavement, he set off at a jog trot, for he wanted to get back to the docks as quickly as possible. A prostitute hailed him and he thrust his hand into his pocket and flung her a dollar bill. She thrust her arm under his, but he shook her roughly away. He did not want to talk with anyone who lived ashore, not even with a girl off the streets, even though she was prepared to give him something in return for what he paid.

He dived into the subway and came out on to streets that smelled of beer, onion, gin, tar, drains and ships, reached the waterfront and the docks. He ran the last short bit until he reached the 'goat', and when he saw old *Anna* he was so pleased that he went up the gangway singing: 'My *Anna* is hulk on the ocean, my *Anna* is hulk on the sea . . .'

The others stood Donkeyman many a round when he signed off in New York. He had stayed in *Anna* a long time and they were all sorry to see him go.

'I'm entitled to sixteen days' holiday and I'll take it while I have the chance,' he had told the Chief half apologetically. Then he had shouldered his kit-bag and walked down the gangway and towards the 'goat' without once looking back. He was in a way sorry to leave *Anna*, but even more he disliked the thought of going to the bottom with sixteen days' holiday in hand.

The new Donkeyman who came aboard in New York looked somewhere between forty and fifty. His entire kit consisted of a small suitcase, worn and dented from much service as stool or pillow when its owner had had to wait at the quayside, in a railway station or in bars where all the seats were occupied. He had not shaved for several days and his old tweed suit was crumpled and stained. He had a black hat that sat straight on his head and was pulled down so far that his big ears were forced outwards. He wore it as people do who only put on a hat for christenings, confirmations, weddings and funerals.

The new Donkeyman was very tipsy. His face was grey with tiredness and his efforts to keep his balance made him grotesquely pompous. As he walked towards the mess, he had to take a quick little sideways step across the deck every now and again in order to stay on his feet.

The docks were shrouded in mist, and the dirty, damp air made everything wet and slippery. But this middle-aged man, drunk as he was, did not have to look where he was treading, even though this was the first time he had trod *Anna*'s deck. He had been aboard so many boats in his life.

He did not greet the others in the mess, but just sat down and groped automatically for the coffee-pot. Slowly and with the utmost care he half filled a dirty cup lying on the table. But he did not drink it, and he did not speak. He did not even answer when the Boy, trying to be pleasant, spoke to him.

Soon after the Boy had said hallo to him, the new Donkeyman, as though he were blind, drew his two hands to the edge of the table, knocking over two cups as he did so. Strong, workman's hands they were with old scars and small, fairly recent burns on them. He took hold of the table's edge and pulled himself to his feet, slowly turned to the door, and those who bothered to look saw his dark shape and black hat swallowed up by the grey mist.

He did not come on watch and so the Greaser was sent to rouse him, but came back to the engine-room saying that it was hopeless: he could not wake him. Then the Chief himself went to the Donkeyman's cabin, but also found it impossible to wake him. No one in the whole world could have got him to open those bloodshot eyes and mutter in a thick voice, as he had when roused to so many watches in so many ships.

The Chief placed finger and thumb on the man's eyelids and carefully parted them. The pupils were dull and rigid. The Chief undid the buttons of the unwashed khaki shirt and put his ear to the skinny chest beneath; then he straightened up and shook his head sadly.

The dead man had a half-empty bottle of whisky in the crook of his arm. The Chief put it on the table. He picked the man's black hat off the floor and pushed his little case tidily against the bulkhead. Then he went to tell the Skipper. A doctor came aboard and said something about heart and shortly afterwards they carried the body across the deck and down the gangway, taking him back the way he had staggered two hours earlier. The Chief trotted along behind the stretcher, carrying the dead man's suitcase and his black hat.

The Skipper got a lift up town with the ambulance, sitting beside the driver as they drove through the dreary streets by the docks to the more lively business quarter. He gave some sort of answers to the driver's many questions. The Skipper could not remember the dead man's name. He racked his brains, but it would not come. He was also wondering if he could get hold of a new donkeyman quickly.

Luck was with the Skipper when he got to the shipping office and three hours later a new donkeyman came aboard *Anna*. He went straight to his cabin and lay there snoring in his bunk, on which clean sheets had been put after the previous occupant had been removed.

Anna was on her way to the Caribbean before the new Donkeyman was due to stand his first watch in the engine-room. The crew should have been in high spirits seeing that they were not to make another crossing immediately. They should have been delighted that they were sailing south to sunshine and warm winds, to blue seas with far fewer U-boats lurking in their depths, to ports with brown-skinned women and cheap drink, to waters where you could lie out on deck without freezing at night and look up at a star-strewn sky before falling asleep. But the thought of the dead donkeyman depressed them. If they had had a bit of talk with him, it would have made everything different. But this man had gone to his cabin and died there without saying a word to anyone aboard: to them he had just been a pale unshaven face under a black hat and then a corpse being carried down the gangway and driven away in an ambulance.

But for this man having died without having spoken to any of them, they would scarcely have concerned themselves with the fact that the anchor had stuck when they were due to raise it and sail from New York. It was a thing that had happened before. Nor would they have thought much of the fact that the Chief was having problems with the engines. That had happened before, and they had had to stop and repair something while at sea.

At supper Bo'sun had flown into a tantrum because the stew was not seasoned enough, although the Cook had used exactly the same amount of salt and pepper as before, when no one had made a fuss.

On the second morning at sea the look-out caught sight of something in the water a cable's length to starboard. Through glasses they could see that it was three men drifting in life-jackets. The sudden change of course aroused the curiosity of those with watch below and soon most of the crew were standing by the rail to help bring the three aboard. The Skipper ordered 'stop', and *Anna* crept towards them, while Bo'sun busily got everything ready to pick them up. But he suddenly went rigid and all the others stood there with mouths half-open and horror in their eyes; for it was three dead men bobbing beside the ship in the calm waters, men long dead, who had been rising and falling in gentle swell or choppy seas for many days and nights. All the hair had gone from their heads. They lay on their backs, only their chests and part of their stomachs breaking the surface. They were in old-fashioned life-belts, their legs hanging vertically as if they were broken. The hairless skulls and faces shone greenish-white just below the water. The three dead men rose and fell in the rhythm of the long swell, rising almost vertically in the wall of each wave so that they looked as if they were about to get up and walk out of the grey-blue water. Then they rolled over the crest and sank into another trough; it was an endless process of being buried and lifted up half-way in a succession of waves. Each time it looked as if they were coming to life and trying to step across to *Anna* lifting and falling in the same rhythm as they.

'We can't do anything with them. They have been in the water too long,' the Skipper said to the First Mate. He took hold of the engine-room telegraph and rang slow astern to prevent the bodies getting into the propellers. When *Anna* was well clear of the three who kept together because, before death came to them, they had tied themselves together with a length of rope, the Skipper rang 'full speed ahead'. He wanted to get away as quickly as he could. In a grim tone he ordered, 'Hard-a-starboard!'

'Hard-a-starboard,' the helmsman repeated.

'120,' said the Skipper.

'120 it is,' said the helmsman.

'Steady so.'

'Steady so.'

And once more *Anna* was on course for the Caribbean.

The men were glum and irritable, and the atmosphere in the mess at mealtimes was explosive. Whatever was said, someone always managed to twist it and start a squabble. Time and again tempers rose to such an extent that the men were on the point of going for each other. The Bo'sun let fly with his tongue at practically nothing, and on the fourth day at sea the otherwise level-headed First Mate got up abruptly from dinner, eyes blazing with anger and cheeks bulging in his flushed face. He had a mouthful of meat and kept his lips together until he got to the galley, where he spat the contents into the slop pail in front of the Steward and Cook.

'Are you ill?' the Steward asked, glaring at him aggressively.

'I will be with the rotten food you provide,' the First Mate replied and went on spitting and swearing.

The Steward flung a ladle to the floor and strode furiously to the saloon where he shouted at the Skipper that he was finished with *Anna* and was going to sign off in the next port. The Skipper just nodded and went on eating.

It was as if the entire ship had been bewitched ever since they left New York. Now they were sailing under a blue sky with a high sun over a blue sea, yet he scarcely recognized the crew. The men just gave a grunt, if that, when they were given an order concerning their duties, and almost everything was done reluctantly and badly. He wondered whether it could be reaction after the nervous strain of the Atlantic crossings. Although they all knew that ships had been sunk in these waters, they did not have the same dread that was ever present when sailing between England and America. Here *Anna* was alone, and in ballast so if she was torpedoed they had a good chance of surviving in the lifeboats or rafts. They would not die of cold as you did so quickly in the North Atlantic.

The Skipper's thoughts went back to the donkeyman who had come aboard and died before he had stood a single watch. Who had gone down to his cabin and lain there in his bunk, rigid – a pale, unshaven face beneath a black hat. This fretful, sinister mood had begun to infect the crew on that misty day when the man's body had been carried down the gangway in New York.

And here in the Caribbean there was too much time to think! And if you thought much, life could begin to appear precious and you might find yourself longing for a normal existence and the thought of *Anna* going back to Atlantic convoy work would become intolerable . . .

It grew hotter every day and the men sweated both on deck and in the engine-room, and swore. They began to hate the ship and the sea and the sky and the ever-receding horizon . . .

On the fifth day out the U-boat alert sounded. The look-out thought he had seen a periscope a short distance abaft the port beam. Course was changed so that *Anna*'s stern was pointing in the direction in which the look-out thought he had glimpsed a periscope. Extra full speed was ordered and those in the engine-room knew at once that there might be U-boats in the vicinity. The engines were asked to give of their utmost. They had to risk a break-down. The whole ship began to quiver as the danger point was exceeded. But the Chief just pressed her along. His was a simple calculation: better to risk the machinery being ruined by overloading and have a chance of escaping the U-boat, than to keep to the safety regulations until a torpedo sent the ship to the bottom. The engines hammered and thudded; pistons and shafts, axles and cranks rising and falling, whirling round, thrusting up and hissing back. 'Sparks' morsed an SOS on medium-wave, but to his dismay there was no reaction; neither from the mainland, nor from Cuba or Haiti came any sign that his message had been picked up; so he switched to short-wave. Almost at once he made contact with an American military base.

The engines were still holding out and the Chief stood on the manœuvre platform thinking that *Anna* had a better heart than many people. It was as if the engines were trying to repay him for having oiled and greased, cleaned and adjusted them, filed and tightened their parts so patiently and devotedly all those years. Now the engines were pounding and hammering and groaning, and he would not have blamed them if they had given up. His own heart was beating irregularly and painfully too, because he was having to maltreat the ship.

'Contact with American military base,' Sparks reported.

'Then perhaps we'll have a US plane overhead before long,' the Skipper replied. He did not say any more. Everyone knew that *Anna* could get clear if the engines would just stand the strain a little longer. They stood with field-glasses to their eyes staring at the waters astern and to either side. Carpenter had the gun ready to fire, and elsewhere others stood with their fingers on the triggers of the machine guns.

When a few more minutes had passed without anything happening, the Chief slowly reduced the number of revolutions to 'full speed', for he had a feeling that a few seconds more of such overloading and the engines might break down.

For another hour *Anna* continued in the same direction, but after that the Skipper felt justified in changing course to head once more for their destination in the Caribbean.

They never discovered whether there had been a U-boat in the area that day; but the look-out insisted that he had seen a periscope.

After this the Skipper noticed that the atmosphere aboard changed. The U-boat scare and *Anna*'s dash for safety had given the men new energy and had brought the old sense of solidarity and comradeship to life again. Now they found pleasure in the sunshine and the heat, and Bo'sun's deep belly-laugh rumbled out once more while he held forth to the Boy about the cheap rum and beautiful women that he could expect where they were going. Those with watch below became suddenly busy washing shirts and trousers and socks, squabbling good-naturedly over buckets and soap.

When the Cook came into the mess at dinner time, no one had any complaints to make about the food. It was corned beef and mash and although Carpenter was always grumpy when there was corned beef and so couldn't say anything nice about it now, he did say: 'Well, Cook, those were fine steaks you found for us that day the Germans were sinking all those ships round us.'

'Ha-ha,' Bo'sun growled. 'You talk like a cook-book.'

The others laughed. The Boy had to clasp his belly and the Cook laughed so much he had to wipe his eyes with his apron.

And *Anna* ploughed on across the blue Caribbean without

anyone noticing that AB had gone silent and no longer spoke. They had all been irritable and depressed after leaving New York and had enough to do dealing with their own depression and despondency. AB was on the watch from eight o'clock until twelve, but did not go to the mess for dinner once his trick at the wheel was over. He felt peculiar and dropped his life-jacket on the boat deck and sat on it. Something inside him was pressing and pressing. He squeezed his forehead with both hands as he fought to keep the icy waves in there from filling his entire head. His eyes were wide open and his teeth clenched. He drew his chin down on to his chest to feel his jaw muscles tightening up by his temples. His mind was like a breakwater crumbling under the onslaught of the ever-fiercer flood in his head. He tried thinking of all the things he feared most and loved most, in order to force the flood back: torpedoes, burning ships, his girl, his wife, his best friend the Carpenter. But their figures shrivelled as soon as he had conjured them up, became hazy shadows which the whirling flood inside his head swept from his consciousness. But he was not going to give up, was not going to lose his self-control, not let those strange foreign forces crush the breakwater.

There was a roaring and crashing inside his head and he could no longer feel his body. He raised his arm to his mouth and bit it until the blood ran, but he felt no pain. Then he pressed the palms of his hands against the deck, but there was no feeling in them and then he put them up and pulled on his hair so as to raise his scalp and stop the flood swamping his brain. Ships were on fire, men burning, men being torn by exploding depth-charges and behaving like dynamited fish in a fjord. And AB wanted to cling to those horrible sights, to what had been reality, but again everything melted and fused into a single white-hot flood . . .

It was hot and the seas calm. Carpenter had stretched out on the poop deck for an afternoon nap. *Anna* swayed gently in the swell lulling him into a pleasant doze in which he could dream of being up in his lighthouse sending its beam of light far out across a sea on which sailed white ships manned by men who were going to have long lives. He was just drifting into sleep when two hands like claws laid fierce hold of his shoulders, and began tearing at him. Carpenter, startled, rolled over on his side and heaved himself to his feet. He took a step forward and found himself face to face with AB. He was just about to tell him off for playing such a stupid violent joke, when he saw that AB's great head was flung back and his eyes fixed and filled with a crazy light. AB's lips moved and Carpenter heard him whisper: 'Can't you see him? Can't you see him?'

'Who?' Carpenter asked, making his voice calm and gentle.

'The devil – standing by the rail there!' AB flung his arms convulsively round the Carpenter and begged him to drive the devil away, to throw him out to the sharks.

Carpenter laid his great hands on the other's shoulders that were quivering with terror. Then in a strong comforting tone he said : 'I'll soon have him in the sea. You can rely on me. You know that . . .'

And Carpenter raised his arm, pointed at the rail, and in a commanding tone called out, 'Off the ship, devil.' Then he lowered his voice and said, 'Look. The nasty thing's gone now.'

AB, who had hidden his face on Carpenter's chest, now slowly raised his head until he could see over the other's broad shoulders. His trembling became less violent. Carpenter took hold of him by one arm, carefully but firmly, and said, 'Let's go to the mess. It must be coffee time.'

AB was not able to hold his cup. It fell out of his hand and the coffee flooded the waxcloth. He was shaking all over. The others at the table could not get a word out. They could not bring themselves to look at that great head and the eyes that did not seem to recognize them, AB's eyes that had always been so friendly and melancholy were now staring and fixed on something no one else could see.

Bo'sun took the coffee-pot and filled up the cups of those near him. The Boy took a dishcloth and wiped up the coffee AB had spilled. Bo'sun stood holding the coffee-pot, uncertain what to do. There was a beseeching look in his eyes as AB did not react. He just continued as before to stare at the bulkhead and something beyond the ship's side.

Boy felt sick with grief and compassion. He had to bring AB back to them, and in as manly a voice as he could manage, said: 'We haven't heard anything about your brown-eyed girl today.'

Fearful but hopeful they all stared at AB. For a moment it looked from his eyes as though he had recovered his reason; then he opened his mouth and in a voice none of them had heard before, he said, 'The girl's no more.'

Bo'sun told the First Mate who reported it to the Skipper. Carpenter was told to take AB to the sick-bay midships, but when they came out on deck, AB resisted and stood pointing out to sea. Then he spoke again, saying that the sea was black and covered over with thousands of white, shiny corpses. Then AB pulled Carpenter with him to the rail and pointed eagerly at a spot not far from the ship's side, saying: 'Do you see my name in that gap among all those crosses put up to our shipmates? Can't you see the letters COME and my name in white on the black surface of the sea?'

Carpenter grunted agreement, and AB became more amenable and went with him to the sick-bay.

They gave him plenty of strong pills and Carpenter sat down to watch beside him, refusing to be relieved. Towards evening he took AB out on to the deck again, thinking it would do him good to have a little fresh air. They stood looking out to sea and AB said that he must go to that empty space among the white crosses, to where his name was written on the surface; but he made no attempt to wrest free of

Carpenter's grasp and jump overboard.

Darkness came suddenly, as it always does in that part of the world, and AB said stammeringly: 'Now God won't see us any more.'

That night he had a fresh violent attack of terror and Carpenter lay down beside him on the outer edge of the bunk like a live wall, until AB grew calmer again.

Next day, Carpenter and the others began almost to hope that AB was going to recover. There was a little more life in his eyes and he talked of signing off as soon as they got to New York. His talk was a bit incoherent and he kept repeating that he must get back to Norway to help his family; but Carpenter considered him calm enough to take on deck and the two men sat there in sunshine and a gentle breeze.

Those who had been with *Anna* a good long time, as most of the crew had, kept coming up to the two men on the hatch in the forepeak to say a word or two to AB. They brought him cigarettes, chocolate and magazines, and the Chief who neither smoked nor read detective thrillers came with a present of a blue tie.

They had all seen men's minds break down under the weight of fear, some jumped overboard in open sea, some were dragged screaming to a hospital ashore; they had seen men dying gradually, a bit each day, under the stress of convoy work. They had felt grief and knew how it increased their own fears; but fresh men had been signed on to occupy the dead or sick man's bunk, had taken his place at table in the mess and stood his watch, and the ship had always gone on sailing.

They could not have said that one shipmate's misfortune or death had grieved them more than another's, but with AB it was all quite different. He and his little girl and wife had become an indispensable part of life aboard. His fantasies and tales about those two and their little house in a village had become necessary for their owns dreams and imaginings. They alone could fill them with pleasant dreams of all that awaited them if peace came and if ever they got home again. So AB was the one they must not lose, not AB whose tales kept them going through the convoys.

So they went to the hatch where he and Carpenter were sitting, stood talking to them in low, friendly tones, while *Anna* ploughed on through the blue Caribbean. After a while AB appeared to be perfectly calm, and when he did speak, it was no longer about the white cross or the devil, but just of signing off, so that he could get home to his wife and child as quickly as possible. It was because AB had mentioned his little girl that Carpenter relaxed his attention and let him go to the WC by himself, while he went below to his cabin for another packet of cigarettes.

But when he got back AB had disappeared. There was no one in the WC. Carpenter ran to the rail to see if there was any excitement among the sharks. Then he raised the alarm.

They set about searching *Anna* from stem to stern. They ran to the cabins, the holds, and the darkest corners of the engine-room; they peered into the lifeboats, ran about calling AB by name. Carpenter was the first to enter the forepeak: he saw no one there and no one answered his call. But the little trapdoor in the deck leading to the chain locker had been raised and placed to one side, and across the dark gaping hole lay a lever and in the middle of the lever was a rope-knot. They knew then, knew that AB was at the end of that rope.

They could not get into the chain locker. There was not room for two bodies in so narrow a space; so Carpenter and Bo'sun each took hold of an end of the lever and lifted it up. First came a short length of rope, then the big heavy head of AB and, as soon as his shoulders were clear of the hole, they seized his arms and heaved the lifeless body right out. Hurriedly they loosened the noose round the thin neck and carried him out and laid him on the hatch in the forepart.

The Mate came running up and started resuscitation. Then Carpenter took over; but no one was allowed to take over from Carpenter. He massaged AB's chest, his neck and belly, raised and lowered his arms. Carpenter was tireless, but he could not bring AB back to life.

Bo'sun split an oar in two and, discarding the blade, put half the shaft under AB's back and on it rolled him to and fro in an attempt to make him breathe, but there was no sign of life. Everyone spoke in low tones, somewhat breathlessly, but they would not admit that AB was dead.

In a hoarse voice Bo'sun said that he had heard that somewhere a man who had hanged himself had been made to breathe by opening an artery. That had made the blood circulate again and the lifeless had come to life. So Bo'sun took AB's arm, rolled up the khaki sleeve and made a deep cut across an artery. A little blood trickled out. They stared beseechingly at AB's face, but it was bluish-pale and dead.

Carpenter lifted his friend up into a sitting position. The great head fell back, and when they bent him forward it fell quickly and heavily on his chest.

They knew that he was dead, but they would not give up, especially Carpenter who held the lifeless body clasped for a long time: he put a mirror to the half-open mouth and stared intently to see if there was any bit of misting on the shiny surface. And even when Carpenter stopped his attempts to make AB breathe again, they seemed unable to recognize that he was dead. They left him lying on the hatch in his brown khaki shirt, faded dungaree trousers and brown shoes, leaving him uncovered as if he was only having a rest on the dirty grey tarpaulin . . .

AB had piled three large cans of paint on top of the other in the narrow hole they used as a storeroom in the forepeak. He had stood on them, put the noose round his neck and kicked the cans away.

The dead man's hands were flecked with rust. So it looked as if for a brief moment when the cans rolled away under his feet he had recovered his senses, pulled himself up by the rope, and then caught hold of the lever across the opening. Then he had lost his grip and the noose had tightened again round his neck.

AB's body lay there until darkness fell. Then Carpenter went to the Steward and was given a blanket with which he carefully covered his dead friend. For one last time he placed his ear against AB's chest and listened; then he looked at the face that was turned, white and rigid, to the stars above the Caribbean. He took AB's cold hand and, half to himself, said: 'Thanks for everything and for the brown-eyed girl . . .'

Carpenter stayed a long time by himself on the fo'c'sle and when he finally went aft they found him standing by himself at the rail. The Boy had his back to him and when Carpenter suddenly asked where the First Mate was, the Boy gave a startled jump and stammered: 'He has hanged himself.'

They were all like that, their minds preoccupied with AB's death. They were restless and walked about, though not to the fore-hatch where AB lay under his blanket. There was no wind and when anyone spoke it was in a low voice. The sea was as quiet as a cemetery.

Next day *Anna* reached the port where she was to load. There were warehouses beside the quay and wretched houses of baked mud lining a single street with a primitive sidewalk of rough planks, one mean bar and small white church on an eminence in the no-man's land between the village and the sugar fields beyond.

The Skipper went ashore to see about burying AB. He had put on his navy-blue uniform and cap with its faded braid, and the sweat poured off him as he parleyed with the priest for a last resting place for AB. The priest was most reluctant to let a person who had taken his own life have a plot within the walls of his churchyard. In fact he had to consider the matter, and would the Skipper come back in a couple of hours?

Back aboard, the Skipper refused to say anything, being afraid that if they heard of the priest's scruples they might storm ashore and go for him.

It was noon and blazing hot when the Skipper went ashore a second time in his uniform, which he wore because there were so few other ways of paying his last respects to AB. The priest was still obstinate, but finally agreed that AB might be buried right up against the churchyard wall, but inside, if the Skipper would sign an undertaking that the Norwegian authorities would fetch his mortal remains as soon as the war was over.

A coffin was brought down to the quayside. They picked AB up to place him in it, but he was too long. They had to undo his laces and take off his brown shoes; then they managed to squeeze the stiff body into the coffin. There was a pane of glass in the lid. They would never forget the last sight they had of AB . . .

The high-wheeled hearse was drawn by two black horses up the uneven, dusty street between its two lines of white-washed little houses with roofs of corrugated iron. Behind it walked *Anna*'s entire crew. First the Skipper with the mates, then the others, and at the rear the Chief and the Boy side by side.

The Skipper made a sort of speech, and that done he picked up a camera he had put on the ground beside him and took photographs of the coffin. He looked sternly, almost threateningly, at the ring of men round the open grave and said that if any of them got back to Norway, they were to tell AB's wife and girl that AB had been killed in an accident on board.

The priest did not put in an appearance, not wanting to have anything to do with an unbeliever and a suicide. The

Skipper picked up the spade and threw a couple of spadefuls of dry sand on to the coffin, saying 'from earth you came and earth you shall become, and from earth you shall rise again'.

Strident trumpet calls splintered the hot air between the houses and were muted on their way to the churchyard, where they swept across the grave like invisible threads of silver; they came from the steps of the bar, where a man had been posted to play his trumpet and tempt the sailors in for a drink.

The men wanted to sing a hymn for AB. There was a lot of throat clearing and coughing, then the Chief struck up 'So take my hands', and those who could, joined in. They stared at the toecaps of their shoes. They were so unused to singing, they made a growling stuttering sound and some were at the end of a line when others were still only in the middle.

Once outside the churchyard they stood avidly drawing in the smoke of their newly lit cigarettes and talking almost in whispers. Then they walked off slowly, as if reluctant to leave AB for ever, heading back towards the harbour, while the trumpet sputtered angry fanfares and occasional plaintive notes.

They went into the bar without anyone actually saying he was in need of a drink, but no one except the Skipper and the Chief felt able to go on board just yet. The bar had a few rickety chairs and bare tables and there were great gaps in the plank floor. There were lots of bottles and innumerable mosquitoes which were even more eager for the seamen than the three girls the owner loosed on them. But no one would have anything to do with the girls. The men sat emptying their glasses and having them refilled.

Carpenter, who was sitting at the same table as Bo'sun, kept rubbing his head, thrusting his fingers into the tangled thatch of his hair. Every now and again he opened his mouth to speak, but it was not until after several glasses that he finally got out what he wanted to say.

'I should never have left AB to get those cigarettes. I shouldn't have done it, never . . .'

It was as if Bo'sun had been expecting something of the kind, for he answered without having to search for words:

'No one could have done anything about it. It was the convoys killed AB. Sooner or later most of us are reduced to wrecks. People like AB, who yearn most and think most, are always the ones to go first. It just takes a bit longer with ones like us, that's all.' He thumped Carpenter's shoulder and before they left the bar most of the crew had come up and done the same.

On the voyage back to the States there was not one squabble in the mess. It was as if they still had AB with them.

Anna's cargo of sugar was discharged in New York, and they were in no doubt where their ship was being sent next, for she was loaded up with bombs, shells, nitro-glycerine, ammunition and various containers brought by US soldiers and stowed below the deck in stout slings. They were in No. 3 hatch, which was specially lined with asbestos.

Anna's crew wondered what the steel containers could have in them to make them so much more dangerous than bombs or TNT . . .

Half the crew signed off in New York, but those who stayed in *Anna* included Carpenter, Bo'sun, the Boy, the Chief and the Cook. The Skipper was ashore a great deal searching the shipping offices for replacements. It was not an easy task because there had been too much talk in the bars about the donkeyman dying and AB hanging himself in the Caribbean. But new men were found and came aboard, and then one day the Skipper came back from the convoy conference and *Anna* sailed out to join the others making up the convoy . . .

Thirty-six grey ships (or was it forty-six this time?) sailed on a grey sea beneath grey skies. In them were over a thousand men in constant expectation of being torpedoed. Old ships and new ships, small ships and large ships sailed for England at seven knots – a slow convoy.

And now it was six days (or was it eight this time?) since they had left the coast of America.

I am one of those who sailed in those convoys, one of those who have been permanently damaged by the mental and physical strain. I have read Per Hansson's book in MS and can assure the reader that he tells the truth about the thousands of Norwegian seamen and what they endured during the war. It is almost as if I had sailed in *Anna*, working and struggling with all the nameless men in her.

I am one of the very few who have been granted a war pension, and I know that many disabled convoy men have been forgotten and let down by society. So it is my hope that *One in Ten Had to Die* will open the eyes of the Norwegian authorities and so make it possible for all disabled wartime seamen to receive recognition for what they did and be granted the pensions they should have had many years ago.

Lief M. Heimstad